W9-CUK-244

STRUCTURE OF MATTER SERIES

MARIA GOEPPERT MAYER

Advisory Editor

MULTIPOLE FIELDS

MULTIPOLE FIELDS

M. E. ROSE

Chief Physicist

Oak Ridge National Laboratory

New York · JOHN WILEY & SONS, Inc.

London · CHAPMAN & HALL, Ltd.

1955

Copyright, 1955
BY
John Wiley & Sons, Inc.

All Rights Reserved

This book or any part thereof must not be reproduced in any form without the written permission of the publisher.

Library of Congress Catalog Card Number: 55-6760

PRINTED IN THE UNITED STATES OF AMERICA

QC 670
R67
Physics
Library

PREFACE

The motivation in writing this book is to be found in the many problems in physics, especially nuclear physics, wherein the basis of the description of the pertinent phenomena is the angular-momentum properties of the systems involved. As examples, the internal conversion process, emission and absorption of electromagnetic radiation (for example, by nuclei), emission of beta particles, angular correlation of radiations emitted by nuclei (or atoms), and the static interactions of nuclear moments with fields due to surrounding ions or other charges may be mentioned. All these problems have played an important role in recent progress in nuclear physics, and, from the point of view of the theoretical description, this is due, in no small measure, to the development of analytical tools particularly well suited for the purpose in hand. These tools involve the application of essentially group theoretic methods: the theory of angular momentum and the application thereto of recent developments in the algebra of irreducible tensors. Because of the power and elegance of these methods their exposition seems highly worth while. In this volume these methods have been utilized in a description of the electromagnetic field. The central theme is the angular-momentum and parity properties (transformation properties) of the multipole fields, inasmuch as it is these aspects of the fields that account for the importance of the role assumed by these fields in our present theories.

In preparing this book I have attempted to make the exposition as self-contained as possible without extensive reproduction of material contained elsewhere. Thus, no very wide knowledge of group theory is necessary, and all the basic results are derived from a comparatively simple starting point. Where a detailed result is obtained elsewhere, and only after a lengthy but straightforward manipulative process, appropriate references are cited. A general knowledge of quantum mechanics and electromagnetic theory is assumed, although, for the sake of continuity, the necessary basis of Maxwell theory is given in the first chapter. The first three chapters, especially Chapters II and III, are devoted to the general development of the theory of multipole fields; the last three chapters are devoted mainly to applications. It is only in these latter chapters that a knowledge of quantum mechanics is necessary.

I am indebted to Dr. L. C. Biedenharn of Yale University for a critical reading of the manuscript. It is to be understood that the responsibility for whatever shortcomings that may exist is solely mine.

M. E. Rose

CONTENTS

I. THE CLASSICAL FIELD EQUATIONS

1. INTRODUCTION

The theory of multipole fields, which has attracted considerable attention in recent years, was first studied by Mie in 1908.[1] At first sight it seems rather remarkable that this essentially classical problem, which, to a large extent, is concerned with the properties of certain types of solutions of the Maxwell field equations, should be of current interest. However, the reasons are not difficult to discern.

One rather obvious reason lies in the fact that the problem is not entirely classical. One of the major problems of modern physics is the quantum theory of the radiation field. Of prime importance in this connection is the fact that the sources (and sinks) of the field are quantum-mechanical systems for which the angular momentum is quantized. Not only the angular momentum but also the parity π of the emitting (and absorbing) nuclei, atoms, etc., are good quantum numbers, that is, constants of the motion. As a consequence the angular momentum and parity of the radiation fields, coupled to such systems, are matters of major concern. The existence of angular momentum in the radiation field has been recognized from a classical point of view for many years, Abraham (14), but the fact that this angular momentum is quantized can be described only in terms of a non-classical theory.

While a quantum description of the field is necessary to account for the conservation of angular momentum in the emission and absorption of electromagnetic radiation as well as in non-radiative electromagnetic transitions,[2] it is important to recognize that there exists a kind of semi-classical counterpart of this description. This arises from two circumstances: (*a*) the correspondence-principle formulation of the interaction energy responsible for emission and absorption and (*b*) the possibility of classifying the Maxwell fields according to their properties under three-dimensional rotations. The correspondence-principle formulation consists in the replacement of the current and charge densities of the source by their quantum-mechanical operator equivalents. These density

[1] A list of references, complete as of 1953, is given in the bibliography on page 95.

[2] For example, internal conversion: Tralli and Goertzel (51); internal pair formation, Rose (49).

operators are coupled to the classical four-potential solutions of the Maxwell equations.[3] The classification of the Maxwell fields to which we refer implies the possibility of representing these fields as irreducible tensors.[4] It is these representations of the Maxwell fields that are referred to as multipole fields, and, indeed, the potentials of a 2^L pole field will be given in terms of irreducible tensors of rank L, sec. 10. Of the many alternative and, of course, equivalent definitions of a multipole field, the definition in terms of the transformation properties is the most pertinent one for the purposes of application to problems of current interest.

The remainder of this chapter is devoted to the classical field equations of the Maxwell theory. The major part of our attention is thereafter concerned with the construction of the multipole fields and a study of their properties. In concluding chapters application is made to a few problems of particular importance for the development of current nuclear theory. These applications, which are concerned with internal conversion accompanying de-excitation of isomeric states of nuclei and the emission of gamma rays by such nuclear states, are discussed primarily as illustrations. Many other applications for which the theory of multipole fields is pertinent will come to mind. Thus, the theory of gamma-ray emission from nuclei can be adapted to a discussion of the radiation emitted by atoms. In the description of nuclear phenomena, the present discussion provides the tools for treating problems of the interaction with electromagnetic radiation at higher energies as well. Examples are the gamma-ray-emission processes accompanying capture of nuclear particles (neutrons or protons) and the inverse process of photodisintegration of nuclei. Other cases of interest for which the formalism presented here is particularly useful are: angular correlation of radiations emitted by nuclei [Biedenharn and Rose (53)], the theory of beta disintegration [Rose (54)], gamma-ray emission by Coulomb excitation of nuclei [Alder and Winther (53)], and the process of internal pair formation already mentioned. The interaction of the static moments (quadrupole moment, for example) of a nucleus with electric and magnetic fields of its environment [Pound (50) and Rose (54)] also finds its natural expression in terms of the formalism given below.

2. THE MAXWELL EQUATIONS

Primarily for the purposes of definition and notation the discussion of this section is devoted to providing the background of Maxwell theory

[3] See, for example, Schiff (49), Chapter X.
[4] Wigner (31).

on which further developments are based. The real (observed) electric and magnetic field strengths are designated by $\bar{E}$ and $\bar{H}$, and, in general, real time-dependent Maxwell fields are denoted by bars. Then, if the source of the field is described by a charge density $\bar{\rho}$, a current density $\bar{\mathbf{j}}$, and a distribution of magnetization $\bar{\mathfrak{M}}$, the Maxwell equations in mixed Gaussian (non-rational) units are

$$c \operatorname{curl} \bar{H} = 4\pi\bar{\mathbf{j}} + \frac{\partial \bar{E}}{\partial t} \tag{1.1a}$$

$$c \operatorname{curl} \bar{E} = -\frac{\partial}{\partial t}(\bar{H} + 4\pi\bar{\mathfrak{M}}) \tag{1.1b}$$

$$\operatorname{div} \bar{E} = 4\pi\bar{\rho} \tag{1.1c}$$

$$\operatorname{div} (\bar{H} + 4\pi\bar{\mathfrak{M}}) = 0 \tag{1.1d}$$

The equation of continuity

$$\operatorname{div} \bar{\mathbf{j}} + \frac{\partial \bar{\rho}}{\partial t} = 0 \tag{1.2}$$

expressing charge conservation, is a consequence of (1.1*a*) and (1.1*c*).

Each of the real fields and source quantities will be expressed in terms of complex scalar and vector functions as follows:

$$\bar{E}(\mathbf{r}, t) = E(\mathbf{r}, t) + E^*(\mathbf{r}, t) \tag{1.3}$$

and

$$E(\mathbf{r}, t) = \mathbf{E}(\mathbf{r})\, e^{-i\omega t} \tag{1.4a}$$

$$E^*(\mathbf{r}, t) = \mathbf{E}^*(\mathbf{r})\, e^{i\omega t} \tag{1.4b}$$

A similar representation expresses $\bar{H}$, $\bar{\rho}$, $\bar{\mathbf{j}}$, and $\bar{\mathfrak{M}}$ as twice the real part of $e^{-i\omega t}$ times $\mathbf{H}$, ρ_0, $\mathbf{j}_0$, and $\mathfrak{M}_0$. Here we restrict our attention to "monochromatic" fields of frequency ω. The special case of a static field is the limit $\omega \to 0$.

With the introduction of the wave number

$$k = \omega/c \tag{1.5}$$

the Maxwell equations become

$$\operatorname{curl} \mathbf{H} = \frac{4\pi}{c}\mathbf{j}_0 - ik\mathbf{E} \tag{1.6a}$$

$$\operatorname{curl} \mathbf{E} = ik(\mathbf{H} + 4\pi\mathfrak{M}_0) \tag{1.6b}$$

$$\operatorname{div} \mathbf{E} = 4\pi\rho_0 \tag{1.6c}$$

$$\operatorname{div} (\mathbf{H} + 4\pi\mathfrak{M}_0) = 0 \tag{1.6d}$$

and the continuity equation is

$$\operatorname{div} \mathbf{j}_0 - i\omega\rho_0 = 0 \tag{1.7}$$

In the usual manner the *vector potential* **A** is introduced by

$$\operatorname{curl} \overline{\mathbf{A}} = \overline{\boldsymbol{H}} + 4\pi\overline{\mathfrak{M}} \tag{1.8}$$

by virtue of (1.1*d*). With

$$\overline{\mathbf{A}} = \mathbf{A}(\mathbf{r})\, e^{-i\omega t} + \mathbf{A}^*(\mathbf{r})\, e^{i\omega t}$$

equation 1.8 is equivalent to

$$\operatorname{curl} \mathbf{A} = \mathbf{H} + 4\pi\mathfrak{M}_0 \tag{1.8$'$}$$

As a consequence of (1.6*b*) we can write

$$\overline{\boldsymbol{E}} = -\frac{1}{c}\frac{\partial\overline{\mathbf{A}}}{\partial t} - \operatorname{grad} \overline{U} \tag{1.9}$$

where $\overline{U}$ is a real scalar (*scalar potential*), and with

$$\overline{U} = U(\mathbf{r})\, e^{-i\omega t} + U^*(\mathbf{r})\, e^{i\omega t}$$

the time-independent form of (1.9) is

$$\mathbf{E} = ik\mathbf{A} - \operatorname{grad} U \tag{1.9$'$}$$

The time-independent field quantities such as **E**, **H**, **A**, and U may be referred to as amplitude functions. Since we deal with these time-independent quantities for the most part, it will be convenient to refer to them as electric and magnetic field strengths, vector and scalar potentials, etc., without further qualification. For each equation involving amplitudes, another is obtained by taking the complex conjugate.

As is well known the purpose in introducing the potentials is to formulate the theory in terms of these alone. Then the field strengths are derivable from (1.8) or (1.8′) and (1.9) or (1.9′). To obtain decoupled wave equations for the potentials it is necessary to impose another restriction, the Lorentz condition:

$$\operatorname{div} \overline{\mathbf{A}} + \frac{1}{c}\frac{\partial\overline{U}}{\partial t} = 0 \tag{1.10}$$

or

$$\operatorname{div} \mathbf{A} - ikU = 0 \tag{1.10$'$}$$

Then, with the aid of the identity

$$\operatorname{curl}\operatorname{curl} = \operatorname{grad}\operatorname{div} - \nabla^2 \tag{1.11}$$

we obtain the well-known wave equations

$$\nabla^2\bar{\mathbf{A}} - \frac{1}{c^2}\frac{\partial^2\bar{\mathbf{A}}}{\partial t^2} = -\frac{4\pi}{c}(\bar{\mathbf{j}} + c \operatorname{curl} \bar{\mathfrak{M}}) \tag{1.12a}$$

and

$$\nabla^2\bar{U} - \frac{1}{c^2}\frac{\partial^2\bar{U}}{\partial t^2} = -4\pi\bar{\rho} \tag{1.12b}$$

The time-independent forms are

$$\nabla^2\mathbf{A} + k^2\mathbf{A} = -(4\pi/c)(\mathbf{j}_0 + c \operatorname{curl} \mathfrak{M}_0) \tag{1.12a'}$$

and

$$\nabla^2 U + k^2 U = -4\pi\rho_0 \tag{1.12b'}$$

In subsequent developments it will not be necessary to explicitly exhibit the decomposition of the current into convection ($\bar{\mathbf{j}}$) and amperian (c curl $\bar{\mathfrak{M}}$) contributions. We may write $\bar{\mathbf{j}}$ for the total current. The continuity equation is then unchanged.

For the case of practical interest the sources of the field are located within a bounded region, and we may also consider that these sources were established within a finite time interval in the past. Then the retarded potential solutions of (1.12a') and (1.12b') are, in this notation,

$$\mathbf{A}(\mathbf{r}) = \frac{1}{c}\int \mathbf{j}_0(\mathbf{r}')\, G_0(\mathbf{r}, \mathbf{r}')\, d\mathbf{r}' \tag{1.13a}$$

$$U(\mathbf{r}) = \int \rho_0(\mathbf{r}')\, G_0(\mathbf{r}, \mathbf{r}')\, d\mathbf{r}' \tag{1.13b}$$

where

$$G_0(\mathbf{r}, \mathbf{r}') = \frac{e^{ik|\mathbf{r}-\mathbf{r}'|}}{|\mathbf{r} - \mathbf{r}'|} \tag{1.14}$$

is the Green's function for the scalar Helmholtz equation:

$$\nabla^2 G_0 + k^2 G_0 = -4\pi\delta(\mathbf{r} - \mathbf{r}') \tag{1.14'}$$

with $\delta(\mathbf{r} - \mathbf{r}')$ the three-dimensional Dirac delta function [e.g., Schiff (49), Chapter III].

For a source wherein $\bar{\mathbf{j}}$ and $\bar{\rho}$ are restricted to a finite region, such that outside this region $\bar{\mathbf{j}} = \bar{\rho} = 0$, the fields outside are given as solutions of the free-space Maxwell equations. These are obtained, of course, from the set (1.1) or (1.6) by setting $\bar{\rho} = \bar{\mathbf{j}} = 0$ and also $\bar{\mathfrak{M}} = 0$.

The time-independent form of the resulting wave equations

$$\nabla^2 \mathbf{A} + k^2 \mathbf{A} = 0 \tag{1.15a}$$

$$\nabla^2 U + k^2 U = 0 \tag{1.15b}$$

are referred to as vector and scalar Helmholtz equations, respectively. The solutions of these equations clearly form a complete set, which can be orthonormalized. Hence, the solutions of the inhomogeneous equations with sources present can be expressed in terms of those of the homogeneous equations.

In fact, a particular solution of (1.15*b*) is

$$U_L^M = f_L(kr)\, Y_L^M(\mathfrak{r}) \tag{1.16}$$

where f_L is $\sqrt{2/\pi}$ times the spherical bessel function,

$$f_L(x) = (1/\sqrt{x})\, J_{L+\frac{1}{2}}(x) \tag{1.17}$$

and $Y_L^M(\mathfrak{r})$ is a (normalized) spherical harmonic depending only on the unit vector $\mathfrak{r}$. For purposes of subsequent application we give the explicit definition:[5]

$$Y_L^M(\mathfrak{r}) = \sqrt{\frac{2L+1}{4\pi}\frac{(L-M)!}{(L+M)!}}\frac{(-\sin\vartheta)^M e^{iM\varphi}}{2^L L!}\left(\frac{d}{d\xi}\right)^{L+M}(\xi^2-1)^L \tag{1.18}$$

where $\xi = \cos\vartheta$, and ϑ, φ are, respectively, the polar and azimuth angles of $\mathfrak{r}$. The solution (1.16) is regular at the origin. A linearly independent solution, irregular at the origin, is

$$V_L^M = g_L(kr)\, Y_L^M(\mathfrak{r}) \tag{1.19}$$

where g_L is defined in terms of the spherical Hankel function of the first kind (outgoing wave):

$$g_L(x) = (1/\sqrt{x}) H_{L+\frac{1}{2}}(x) \tag{1.20}$$

Note that

$$Y_L^{M*} = (-)^M Y_L^{-M} \tag{1.21}$$

Then the well-known expansion of the Green's function G_0 is

$$G_0 = 2\pi^2 ik \sum_{L=0}^{\infty} \sum_{M=-L}^{L} U_L^{M*}(\mathbf{r}_<)\, V_L^M(\mathbf{r}_>) \tag{1.22}$$

in a self-explanatory notation. If this result is used in (1.13*a*) and (1.13*b*) then in the region $r > r'$ the solution is expressed as a sum of

[5] Cf. Appendix A.

outgoing waves, solutions of (1.15b), multiplied by constants of the form

$$\int U_L^M(\mathbf{r}') \, \rho_0(\mathbf{r}') \, d\mathbf{r}' \qquad\qquad (1.23)$$

$$= \sqrt{\tfrac{2}{\pi}} \int j_L(kr) \, Y_L^M(\hat{r}') \, \rho(\hat{r}') \, d\hat{r}'$$

which are characteristic of the source. Since expressions like (1.23) give various moments of the charge distribution they are referred to as multipole moments. However, it is to be emphasized that the solutions of (1.12) obtained in this way are not yet represented in terms of multipole fields.

3. GAUGE INVARIANCE

Since the starting point of these considerations is the Maxwell equations 1.1 wherein no potentials but only field strengths occur, it is clear that two sets of potentials $\overline{\mathbf{A}}$, $\overline{U}$ and $\overline{\mathbf{A}}'$, $\overline{U}'$ which yield the same field strengths are physically equivalent. Thus, if

$$\overline{\mathbf{A}}' = \overline{\mathbf{A}} + \nabla \overline{S} \qquad\qquad (1.24a)$$

$$\overline{U}' = \overline{U} - \frac{1}{c}\frac{\partial \overline{S}}{\partial t} \qquad\qquad (1.24b)$$

or, in terms of time-independent potentials,

$$\mathbf{A}' = \mathbf{A} + \nabla S \qquad\qquad (1.25a)$$

$$U' = U + ikS \qquad\qquad (1.25b)$$

then, by (1.8) or (1.8$'$) and (1.9) or (1.9$'$), the two sets of potentials are equivalent. The transformation (1.24) or (1.25) is called a gauge transformation.

In order that the primed or gauge-transformed potentials satisfy the same wave equations (1.12), it is necessary and sufficient that the Lorentz condition (1.10) be satisfied in the primed gauge. This requires that the gauge function $\overline{S}$ be a solution of the homogeneous wave equation.

$$\nabla^2 \overline{S} - \frac{1}{c^2}\frac{\partial^2 \overline{S}}{\partial t^2} = 0 \qquad\qquad (1.26)$$

or

$$\nabla^2 S + k^2 S = 0 \qquad\qquad (1.26')$$

It is clear that a gauge transformation is equivalent to adding a solution of the homogeneous wave equation to (1.13a) and (1.13b).

In the free-space case it is possible to gauge-transform the scalar potential to zero. That is,

$$U' = 0 \qquad S = (i/k)U \tag{1.27}$$

Then div $\mathbf{A}' = 0$. This is referred to as the *solenoidal* gauge. It is not possible to use this gauge where there are sources.

A field of the form $\overline{\mathbf{A}}' - \overline{\mathbf{A}}$, $\overline{U}' - \overline{U}$, that is, one whose vector and scalar potentials are

$$\overline{\mathbf{A}}_l = \nabla \overline{S} \tag{1.28a}$$

$$\overline{U}_l = -\frac{1}{c}\frac{\partial \overline{S}}{\partial t} \tag{1.28b}$$

is called a *longitudinal* field—and corresponds to zero field strengths. Note that for the electrostatic field a time-independent potential must be added to (1.28*b*).

4. PARITY OF THE MAXWELL FIELD

An important consideration in the following is the property of the Maxwell field under coordinate inversion. We define the parity operator Π by

$$\Pi \mathbf{E}(\mathbf{r}) = \mathbf{E}(-\mathbf{r}) \tag{1.29}$$

and similarly for any other field quantity. If we consider the free-space wave equation it is clear that the operator $\nabla^2 - (1/c^2)\,\partial^2/\partial t^2$ commutes with Π. Hence if $\mathbf{A}(\mathbf{r})$ is a solution, $\mathbf{A}(-\mathbf{r})$ is also a solution. Consequently

$$\mathbf{A}_{\pm}(\mathbf{r}) = \mathbf{A}(\mathbf{r}) \pm \mathbf{A}(-\mathbf{r})$$

are solutions and are, moreover, eigenfunctions of the parity operator Π:

$$\Pi \mathbf{A}_{\pm} = \pm \mathbf{A}_{\pm} \tag{1.30}$$

In fact, since $\Pi^2 = 1$ it is clear that ± 1 are the only eigenvalues of Π.

For those fields which have even (or odd) parity in $\mathbf{A}$, that is, the eigenvalue of $\Pi = +1$ (or -1) respectively, the magnetic field strength is odd (or even) and the electric field strength is even (or odd). The present interest in parity properties stems from the fact that the multipole fields are eigenfunctions of the parity operator. It will be convenient to define the parity of a multipole field as the parity of $\mathbf{H}$. Thus, if $\Pi\mathbf{H} = \pm\mathbf{H}$ the upper sign will imply even parity and the lower odd parity.

5. DUAL FIELDS

We again consider the free-space Maxwell equations. It is evident that if $\bar{E}$ and $\bar{H}$ are solutions, then $\bar{E}'$ and $\bar{H}'$ are also solutions if

$$\bar{E}' = \pm\bar{H} \qquad \bar{H}' = \mp\bar{E} \tag{1.31}$$

where either the upper or lower signs are to be used. The field $\bar{E}'$, $\bar{H}'$ is *dual* to the field $\bar{E}$, $\bar{H}$. Clearly, apart from an irrelevant overall sign, $\bar{E}$, $\bar{H}$ is dual to $\bar{E}'$, $\bar{H}'$.

From the considerations of the preceding section it is clear that the parity of any field and its dual are of opposite character.

It may also be pointed out at this juncture that the energy flux, total energy, and angular momentum of the Maxwell field are invariant under the dual transformation. The instantaneous Poynting flux is

$$\mathbf{N} = (c/4\pi)(\bar{E} \times \bar{H})$$

and for the time-average Poynting flux we have

$$\langle\mathbf{N}\rangle = (c/2\pi)\,\mathrm{Re}\,(\mathbf{E} \times \mathbf{H}^*) \tag{1.32}$$

where Re means "real part of."

The energy density is

$$w = (c/8\pi)(\bar{E}^2 + \bar{H}^2)$$

and for the time average we obtain

$$\langle w\rangle = (c/4\pi)(\mathbf{E}\cdot\mathbf{E}^* + \mathbf{H}\cdot\mathbf{H}^*) \tag{1.33}$$

The density of angular momentum is

$$\mathbf{g} = (1/c^2)\mathbf{r} \times \mathbf{N}$$

and the time average is

$$\langle\mathbf{g}\rangle = (1/4\pi c)\mathbf{r} \times (\mathbf{E} \times \mathbf{H}^* + \mathbf{E}^* \times \mathbf{H}) \tag{1.34}$$

Each of these $\mathbf{N}$, w, and $\mathbf{g}$, or their time averages, is invariant under the transformation (1.31).

II. THE MULTIPOLE FIELDS

6. THE ANGULAR-MOMENTUM OPERATORS[1]

There is a very intimate connection between the theory of angular momentum and the description of multipole fields. The fact that the multipole fields are eigenfunctions of the angular-momentum operators introduced below is the very fact that we wish to exploit.

The general angular-momentum operators may be defined as a set of three hermitian operators J_x, J_y, and J_z with the commutation rules[2]

$$J_yJ_z - J_zJ_y = iJ_x \tag{2.1a}$$

$$J_zJ_x - J_xJ_z = iJ_y \tag{2.1b}$$

$$J_xJ_y - J_yJ_x = iJ_z \tag{2.1c}$$

or, written more succinctly,

$$\mathbf{J} \times \mathbf{J} = i\mathbf{J} \tag{2.2}$$

Some examples are:

(*a*) The orbital angular-momentum operator:

$$\mathbf{L} = -i\mathbf{r} \times \nabla \tag{2.3}$$

(*b*) The Pauli spin matrices:

$$\frac{1}{2}\sigma_x = \frac{1}{2}\begin{pmatrix} 0 & 1 \\ 1 & 0 \end{pmatrix} \quad \frac{1}{2}\sigma_y = \frac{1}{2}\begin{pmatrix} 0 & -i \\ i & 0 \end{pmatrix} \quad \frac{1}{2}\sigma_z = \frac{1}{2}\begin{pmatrix} 1 & 0 \\ 0 & -1 \end{pmatrix} \tag{2.4}$$

(*c*) The "spin" matrices for a vector field:

$$S_x = \begin{pmatrix} 0 & 0 & 0 \\ 0 & 0 & -i \\ 0 & i & 0 \end{pmatrix} \qquad S_y = \begin{pmatrix} 0 & 0 & i \\ 0 & 0 & 0 \\ -i & 0 & 0 \end{pmatrix} \qquad S_z = \begin{pmatrix} 0 & -i & 0 \\ i & 0 & 0 \\ 0 & 0 & 0 \end{pmatrix} \tag{2.5}$$

These matrices are considered further in sec. 9.

[1] A much more complete discussion of the material in this section is given in Condon and Shortley (35), Chapter III.

[2] The angular-momentum operators of quantum mechanics are identical with these when the former are expressed in units of $\hbar$, i.e., Planck's constant divided by 2π.

It is clear that if $\mathbf{J}_1$ and $\mathbf{J}_2$ are angular-momentum operators then $\mathbf{J}_1 + \mathbf{J}_2$ is also an angular-momentum operator. It is also evident that if $\mathbf{J}$ is an angular-momentum operator then a unitary transformation generates another angular-momentum operator $\mathbf{J}'$:

$$\mathbf{J}' = C\mathbf{J}C^{-1} \tag{2.6}$$

where C is a non-singular matrix, or in general, an operator for which the inverse C^{-1} exists. Consequently, (2.4) and (2.5) are special representations.

The square of the total angular-momentum operator $\mathbf{J}^2$ is defined by

$$\mathbf{J}^2 = J_x^2 + J_y^2 + J_z^2 \tag{2.7}$$

It is recognized that

$$-\mathbf{L}^2 = \frac{1}{\sin\vartheta}\frac{\partial}{\partial\vartheta}\sin\vartheta\frac{\partial}{\partial\vartheta} + \frac{1}{\sin^2\vartheta}\frac{\partial^2}{\partial\varphi^2} \tag{2.8}$$

that is, the Laplace operator on the unit sphere, commutes with ∇^2 and therefore with $\Omega \equiv \nabla^2 + k^2$. Also $\boldsymbol{\sigma}^2 = 3$ and $\mathbf{S}^2 = 2$ commute with Ω. The same follows for $\mathbf{J}^2$, where $\mathbf{J} = \mathbf{L} + \mathbf{S}$, or $\mathbf{L} + \frac{1}{2}\boldsymbol{\sigma}$, since each component of $\boldsymbol{\sigma}$, $\mathbf{S}$, and $\mathbf{L}$ commutes with Ω. Also the commutator $\mathbf{J}^2 J_i - J_i \mathbf{J}^2 = 0$ $(i = x, y, z)$. It follows that if ψ_j^m is an eigenfunction of Ω (with eigenvalue 0 or otherwise) then the matrix whose elements are

$$(\psi_{j'}^{m'}|\mathbf{J}^2|\psi_j^m)$$

can be diagonalized simultaneously with the matrix with elements

$$(\psi_{j'}^{m'}|J_i|\psi_j^m)$$

where J_i is any *one* component of $\mathbf{J}$. If J_i is chosen to be J_z we have

$$\begin{aligned} \mathbf{J}^2\psi_j^m &= \eta_j\psi_j^m \\ J_z\psi_j^m &= m\,\psi_j^m \end{aligned} \tag{2.9}$$

The eigenvalues η_j and m are readily determined. From (2.9)

$$(J_x^2 + J_y^2)\,\psi_j^m = (\eta_j - m^2)\,\psi_j^m$$

and since the eigenvalues of $\mathbf{J}^2$ and of $J_x^2 + J_y^2$ are non-negative it follows that $0 \le |m| \le \eta_j^{1/2}$. Also from (2.1)

$$J_z J_\pm = J_\pm(J_z \pm 1)$$

where we define

$$J_\pm = J_x \pm iJ_y$$

Consequently, $J_\pm\psi_j^m = 0$ or is proportional to $\psi_j^{m\pm1}$. In general J_+ is an operator increasing the projection (magnetic) quantum number (m) by unity and J_- lowers m by unity. Thus for each η_j there is a set of simultaneous eigenfunctions of $\mathbf{J}^2$, J_z with successive m values differing by unity. The set of m values is bounded for given j by $\pm\eta_j^{1/2}$. Hence, there is a minimum m, m_1 say, for which

$$J_- \psi_j^{m_1} = 0 \tag{2.10a}$$

and a maximum m, m_2 say, for which

$$J_+ \psi_j^{m_2} = 0 \tag{2.10b}$$

Equation 2.10a gives

$$J_+J_- \psi_j^{m_1} = (\mathbf{J}^2 - J_z^2 + J_z)\,\psi_j^{m_1} = 0$$

or

$$\eta_j - m_1^2 + m_1 = 0 \tag{2.11a}$$

Similarly, from (2.10b),

$$\eta_j - m_2^2 - m_2 = 0 \tag{2.11b}$$

whence

$$(m_1 + m_2)(m_1 - m_2 - 1) = 0$$

Therefore $m_1 = -m_2$, and since $m_2 - m_1$ is a non-negative integer, which is written as $2j$ with $j = 0, \frac{1}{2}, 1, \frac{3}{2} \cdots$, it follows that m is an integer (half-odd integer) whenever j is integer (half-odd integer) and that

$$-j \leq m \leq j \tag{2.12}$$

From (2.11)

$$\eta_j = j(j + 1) \tag{2.13}$$

For the examples quoted above:
(a) If $\mathbf{J} = \mathbf{L}$, $\psi_j^m = Y_L^m$ and $j = L = 0, 1, 2 \cdots$.
(b) Taking $\mathbf{J} = \frac{1}{2}\sigma$, $j = \frac{1}{2}$ and

$$\psi_j^{1/2} = \begin{pmatrix}1\\0\end{pmatrix} \qquad \psi_j^{-1/2} = \begin{pmatrix}0\\1\end{pmatrix}$$

(c) Here $j = 1$. A representation of the eigenfunctions will be given in sec. 9.

In the general case, the matrix elements of $J_\pm$ are readily found. With ψ_j^m orthonormal and

$$J_\pm \psi_j^m = \Gamma_\pm \psi_j^{m\pm1}$$

we have, with $J_\pm^* = J_\mp$ (where the asterisk on an operator means hermitian conjugate),

$$|\Gamma_\pm|^2 = (\psi_j^m|J_\mp J_\pm|\psi_j^m) = (\psi_j^m|\mathbf{J}^2 - J_z(J_z \pm 1)|\psi_j^m)$$

$$= (j \mp m)(j \pm m + 1)$$

The phase is chosen so that

$$\Gamma_\pm = \sqrt{(j \mp m)(j \pm m + 1)}$$

or

$$J_\pm \psi_j^m = \sqrt{(j \mp m)(j \pm m + 1)}\, \psi_j^{m\pm 1} \tag{2.14}$$

This choice of phase is consistent with the definition (1.18) as well as with other widely used conventions, Condon and Shortley (35), Racah (42) and (43).

7. COUPLING OF TWO ANGULAR MOMENTA

In most physical problems two (or more) angular momenta which couple together to form a resultant are dealt with. Examples are the orbital and intrinsic spin angular momenta of a single particle, the total angular momenta of a system of two particles, or the angular momenta of a particle and the radiation which it emits (or absorbs). In these cases the angular momenta $\mathbf{j}_1$ and $\mathbf{j}_2$ are in different spaces and they couple together to give a resultant angular momentum $\mathbf{j}$. The respective projection quantum numbers are m_1, m_2, and m. The eigenfunctions in the representation for which $\mathbf{j}_1^2$, $\mathbf{j}_2^2$, j_{1z}, and j_{2z} are diagonal are $\psi_{j_1}^{m_1}\psi_{j_2}^{m_2}$, where the direct product is to be taken. The eigenfunctions in the representation for which $\mathbf{j}_1^2$, $\mathbf{j}_2^2$, $\mathbf{j}^2$, and $j_z = j_{1z} + j_{2z}$ are diagonal are ψ_j^m. The two representations are then connected by a unitary transformation:

$$\psi_j^m = \sum_{m_1 m_2} C(j_1 j_2 j; m_1 m_2 m)\, \psi_{j_1}^{m_1}\psi_{j_2}^{m_2} \tag{2.15}$$

and the C-coefficients are variously called vector-addition coefficients, Clebsch-Gordan coefficients, or Wigner coefficients [see Wigner (31)].[3] A well-known example of the transformation in question is the passage from the weak-field representation (in which the spin-orbit coupling or hyperfine structure interactions are diagonal) to the strong-field representation [wherein the coupling energy to an external magnetic field is diagonal; see Bethe (33)].[4]

[3] The C-coefficient, as we shall call it, is written as $(j_1 j_2 m_1 m_2 | j_1 j_2 j m)$ in Condon and Shortley (35).

[4] Note that the phase convention used in this reference differs from the one adopted here.

Upon application of the j_z operator to (2.15) it is evident that the condition

$$m_1 + m_2 = m \tag{2.16}$$

must be fulfilled by all the C-coefficients. Henceforth, the third projection quantum number will be omitted inasmuch as the condition (2.16) will always be understood. This condition implies the presence of a factor $\delta_{m_1+m_2,m}$, and the sum over m_2, say, may be carried out at once.

The choice of phase implied by (2.14) is consistent with real C-coefficients. Then from

$$(\psi_j^m, \psi_{j'}^{m'}) = \delta_{jj'}\,\delta_{mm'} = \sum_{m_1}\sum_{m_1'} C(j_1j_2j; m_1, m-m_1) \times C(j_1j_2j'; m_1', m'-m_1')\,\delta_{m_1m_1'}\,\delta_{m-m_1,m'-m_1'}$$

we obtain

$$\sum_{m_1} C(j_1j_2j; m_1, m-m_1)\, C(j_1j_2j'; m_1, m-m_1) = \delta_{jj'} \tag{2.17}$$

This result is simply an expression of the unitary property of the C-coefficients. For the same reason there is obtained

$$\sum_{j} C(j_1j_2j; m_1, m-m_1)\, C(j_1j_2j; m_1', m'-m_1') = \delta_{m_1m_1'}\,\delta_{mm'} \tag{2.18}$$

from which it follows that

$$\psi_{j_1}^{m_1}\psi_{j_2}^{m_2} = \sum_j C(j_1j_2j; m_1m_2)\,\psi_j^{m_1+m_2} \tag{2.19}$$

It is easy to see that, when the two angular momenta $\mathbf{j}_1$ and $\mathbf{j}_2$ are coupled, the resultant $\mathbf{j}$ is associated with angular momenta

$$j = |j_1 - j_2|, |j_1 - j_2| + 1 \cdots j_1 + j_2 \tag{2.20}$$

that is, the eigenvalue of $\mathbf{j}^2$ is $j(j+1)$, where the permitted values of j are given by (2.20). The maximum value $j_1 + j_2$ follows from (2.16) and the fact that the maximum values of m_1 and m_2 are j_1 and j_2 respectively. Since there are $2j+1$ linearly independent eigenfunctions associated with the total angular-momentum quantum number j and since a unitary transformation does not change the number of linearly independent eigenfunctions the minimum value of j, j_m say, is given by

$$\sum_{j_m}^{j_1+j_2} (2j+1) = (2j_1+1)(2j_2+1)$$

Since $j_m \geq 0$, the result $j_m = |j_1 - j_2|$ follows immediately. As a consequence it must be understood that the C-coefficient vanishes unless the three momenta j_1, j_2, and j form a triangle. We will say that a triangular condition applies to three quantities a_1, a_2, a_3 if

$$|a_j - a_k| \leq a_i \leq a_j + a_k$$

where a_i, a_j, and a_k are any permutation of a_1, a_2, and a_3. The triangular condition is obviously symmetric in a_1, a_2, a_3. This condition will be denoted by $\Delta(a_1a_2a_3)$.

A derivation of the explicit form of the C-coefficient in terms of the parameters upon which it depends has been given by Wigner (31). From this explicit representation[5] Racah (42) was able to obtain the following symmetry relations:

$$C(j_1j_2j_3; m_1m_2) = (-)^{j_1+j_2-j_3} C(j_2j_1j_3; m_2m_1) \tag{2.20a}$$

$$C(j_1j_2j_3; m_1m_2) = (-)^{j_1+j_2-j_3} C(j_1j_2j_3; -m_1, -m_2) \tag{2.20b}$$

$$(2j_2 + 1)^{1/2} C(j_1j_2j_3; m_1m_2) = (-)^{j_1-m_1}(2j_3 + 1)^{1/2} C(j_1j_3j_2; m_1, -m_3) \tag{2.20c}$$

$$(2j_1 + 1)^{1/2} C(j_1j_2j_3; m_1m_2) = (-)^{j_2+m_2}(2j_3 + 1)^{1/2} C(j_3j_2j_1; -m_3, m_2) \tag{2.20d}$$

$$(2j_1 + 1)^{1/2} C(j_1j_2j_3; m_1m_2) = (-)^{j_1-j_3+m_2}(2j_3 + 1)^{1/2} C(j_2j_3j_1; m_2, -m_3) \tag{2.20e}$$

where $m_3 = m_1 + m_2$ and (2.20e) is a consequence of (2.20d and a). Similarly, (2.20d) can be obtained from (2.20a) and (2.20c). From these symmetry relations it follows that

$$C(l_1l_2l_3; 00) = 0 \tag{2.21}$$

unless $l_1 + l_2 + l_3 \equiv 0 \pmod 2$. Of course, this condition arises only when l_1, l_2, and l_3 are integers. In subsequent applications the parity selection rule will be contained in a C-coefficient of this type. With our choice of phase it also follows that[6]

$$C(j_10j_3; m_1m_2) = \delta_{j_1j_3}\,\delta_{m_20} \tag{2.21'}$$

It will subsequently be seen that we may often dispense with a knowledge of numerical values of the C-coefficients. However, one particular

[5] Cf. Appendix B.
[6] Cf. Appendix A.

case is useful for our purposes. This is $C(j_1 1 j; m-m_2, m_2)$ which is given in Table I. Other cases are given in Condon and Shortley (35).

TABLE I. Values of $C(j_1 1 j; m-m_2, m_2)$

$j =$	$m_2 = 1$	$m_2 = 0$	$m_2 = -1$
$j_1 + 1$	$\sqrt{\frac{(j_1+m)(j_1+m+1)}{(2j_1+1)(2j_1+2)}}$	$\sqrt{\frac{(j_1-m+1)(j_1+m+1)}{(2j_1+1)(j_1+1)}}$	$\sqrt{\frac{(j_1-m)(j_1-m+1)}{(2j_1+1)(2j_1+2)}}$
j_1	$-\sqrt{\frac{(j_1+m)(j_1-m+1)}{2j_1(j_1+1)}}$	$\frac{m}{\sqrt{j_1(j_1+1)}}$	$\sqrt{\frac{(j_1-m)(j_1+m+1)}{2j_1(j_1+1)}}$
$j_1 - 1$	$\sqrt{\frac{(j_1-m)(j_1-m+1)}{2j_1(2j_1+1)}}$	$-\sqrt{\frac{(j_1-m)(j_1+m)}{j_1(2j_1+1)}}$	$\sqrt{\frac{(j_1+m+1)(j_1+m)}{2j_1(2j_1+1)}}$

8. THE TRANSFORMATION PROPERTIES UNDER ROTATION

If an eigenfunction ψ_j^m of $\mathbf{J}^2$ and J_z is described in terms of a second coordinate system which differs from the first by a rotation, it is clear that since the rotation in general alters the direction of the quantization axis z, and because $\mathbf{J}^2$ is an invariant operator under rotations, the eigenfunction in the rotated frame of reference $(\psi_j^m)'$ will be a linear combination of ψ_j^m with different m values but the same j. The coefficients will depend on j and on the parameters fixing the rotation. For the latter we use the Euler angles α, β, γ, and the rotation is carried out as follows: First a rotation of γ about the z-axis is carried out, then a rotation about the y-axis through an angle β, finally a rotation through an angle α about the z-axis.[6]

We designate the eigenfunction obtained from ψ_j^m after the first rotation by $R_\gamma \psi_j^m$. Then

$$R_\gamma \psi_j^m = e^{iJ_z\gamma} \psi_j^m = e^{im\gamma} \psi_j^m \tag{2.22}$$

This is a special case of the general relation [6]

$$R \psi_j^m = e^{i\mathbf{n}\cdot\mathbf{J}\theta} \psi_j^m \equiv \sum_{\nu=0}^{\infty} \frac{(i\mathbf{n}\cdot\mathbf{J}\theta)^\nu}{\nu!} \psi_j^m \tag{2.23}$$

which describes the effect on the ψ_j^m of a rotation through an angle θ about the direction $\mathbf{n}$. Indeed, (2.23) can be used to define the angular-momentum operator $\mathbf{J}$.

The second rotation gives

$$R_\beta R_\gamma \psi_j^m = e^{im\gamma} R_\beta \psi_j^m \equiv e^{im\gamma} \sum_{m'} d_{m'm}^j(\beta) \psi_j^{m'} \tag{2.24}$$

Finally

$$(\psi_j^m)' = R_\alpha R_\beta R_\gamma \, \psi_j^m = e^{im\gamma} \sum_{m'} e^{im'\alpha} \, d^j_{m'm}(\beta) \, \psi_j^{m'}$$

If we represent the matrix for the complete rotation by $D^j(\alpha\beta\gamma)$, that is,

$$(\psi_j^m)' = \sum_{m'} D^j_{m'm}(\alpha\beta\gamma) \, \psi_j^{m'} \tag{2.25}$$

then

$$D^j_{m'm}(\alpha\beta\gamma) = e^{im'\alpha} \, d^j_{m'm}(\beta) \, e^{im\gamma} \tag{2.26}$$

The (real) matrix element $d^j_{m'm}(\beta)$ can be given explicitly [Wigner (31)] by [5]

$$d^j_{m'm}(\beta) = \sqrt{\frac{(j-m)!(j+m')!}{(j+m)!(j-m')!}} \, \frac{\cos^{2j+m-m'} \frac{1}{2}\beta \sin^{m'-m} \frac{1}{2}\beta}{(m'-m)!}$$

$$\times \, {}_2F_1(m'-j, \, -m-j; \, m'-m+1; \, -\tan^2 \tfrac{1}{2}\beta) \tag{2.27}$$

where the hypergeometric function ${}_2F_1$ is a finite polynomial of degree $j + m$ or $j - m'$ (whichever is smaller) in $\tan^2 \frac{1}{2}\beta$. The result (2.27) applies for $m' \geq m$. For $m > m'$ the corresponding result may be obtained from the unitary property of D. Since the rotation inverse to $\alpha\beta\gamma$ is $-\gamma$, $-\beta$, $-\alpha$ we have

$$[D^j_{m'm}]^{-1} = D^{j*}_{mm'}(\alpha\beta\gamma) = D^j_{m'm}(-\gamma, \, -\beta, \, -\alpha) \tag{2.28}$$

We also observe that

$$d^j_{m'm}(\pi - \beta) = (-)^{j-m'} d^j_{m', \, -m}(\beta) \tag{2.29}$$

and

$$D^j_{m'm} = (-)^{m'-m} D^{j*}_{-m', \, -m} \tag{2.29'}$$

since $d^j_{mm'}(\beta) = d^j_{m'm}(-\beta) = (-)^{m-m'} d^j_{m'm}(\beta)$.

From the definition that an eigenfunction ψ_j^m transforms under D^j, the $(2j + 1)$ dimensional representation of the rotation group, we obtain an important property of the D^j. Performing a rotation on the eigenfunctions in (2.19) we have

$$\sum_{\mu_1\mu_2} D^{j_1}_{\mu_1 m_1} \, D^{j_2}_{\mu_2 m_2} \, \psi_{j_1}^{\mu_1} \, \psi_{j_2}^{\mu_2} = \sum_j C(j_1 j_2 j; \, m_1 m_2) \sum_\mu D^j_{\mu m} \, \psi_j^\mu$$

where $m = m_1 + m_2$ and $\mu = \mu_1 + \mu_2$. Using (2.15) and the linear independence of the $\psi_{j_i}^{m_i}$ we find

$$D^{j_1}_{\mu_1 m_1} \, D^{j_2}_{\mu_2 m_2} = \sum_j C(j_1 j_2 j; \, m_1 m_2) \, C(j_1 j_2 j; \, \mu_1 \mu_2) \, D^j_{\mu m} \tag{2.30}$$

where $\Delta(j_1 j_2 j)$ applies. The arguments of all the D matrices are α, β, γ. Equation 2.30 is known as the Clebsch-Gordan series.

We now apply (2.25) in the special case of the eigenfunctions of the orbital angular momentum, namely,

$$Y_L^M(\vartheta'\varphi') = \sum_m D_{mM}^L(\alpha\beta\gamma)\, Y_L^m(\vartheta\varphi)$$

where the primed and unprimed coordinates refer to rotated and primary reference frames, respectively. If this result is compared with spherical harmonic addition theorem

$$Y_L^0(\vartheta'\varphi') = \sqrt{\frac{4\pi}{2L+1}} \sum_m Y_L^{m*}(-\beta, -\alpha)\, Y_L^m(\vartheta\varphi)$$

it follows that

$$D_{m0}^L(\alpha\beta\gamma) = \sqrt{\frac{4\pi}{2L+1}}\, (-)^m\, Y_L^m(\beta\alpha) \tag{2.31}$$

Of course, γ does not appear in this result. Substituting (2.31) in (2.30) we obtain the coupling rule

$$Y_{L_1}^{m_1} Y_{L_2}^{m_2} = \sum_L \sqrt{\frac{(2L_1+1)(2L_2+1)}{4\pi(2L+1)}} \times C(L_1L_2L; 00)\, C(L_1L_2L; m_1m_2)\, Y_L^{m_1+m_2} \tag{2.32}$$

where the arguments of all the spherical harmonics are the same. Here we have used (2.20*b*) and (2.21). Equation 2.32 gives the convenient result for the integral, over the unit sphere, of three spherical harmonics

$$(Y_L^m, Y_{L_1}^{m_1} Y_{L_2}^{m_2}) = \sqrt{\frac{(2L_1+1)(2L_1+1)}{4\pi(2L+1)}} \times C(L_1L_2L; 00)\, C(L_1L_2L; m_1m_2)\, \delta_{m_1+m_2,m} \tag{2.33}$$

In comparing (2.32) and (2.19) note that in the former case the eigenfunctions are in the same space whereas in the latter case they are in different spaces. The triangular condition $\Delta(L_1L_2L)$ and the parity rule $L_1 + L_2 + L =$ even integer are well known and appear in the C-coefficients in (2.33).

9. THE IRREDUCIBLE TENSORS ON THE UNIT SPHERE

Before defining the multipole fields it is necessary to introduce one further definition. If a set of $2L + 1$ functions (L integer) transform under rotations according to the representation D^L these $2L + 1$ functions constitute the components of an *irreducible tensor* of rank L.

If we consider two eigenfunctions $\psi_{L_1}^{M_1}$ and $\psi_{L_2}^{M_2}$ which respectively diagonalize the square and z-component of the operators $\mathbf{L}_1$ and $\mathbf{L}_2$, then, from the Clebsch-Gordan series (2.30), the direct product $\psi_{L_1}^{M_1}\psi_{L_2}^{M_2}$ is not an irreducible tensor but is instead a superposition of tensors of rank L where $|L_1 - L_2| \leq L \leq L_1 + L_2$.[7] However, from the discussion of secs. 7 and 8 it is clear that the particular linear combination of the $(2L_1 + 1)(2L_2 + 1)$ tensor components which is represented in (2.15) is an irreducible tensor.

We now define the *multipole fields* for a 2^L pole as those solutions of free-space Maxwell equations which transform under D^L and which, moreover, are eigenfunctions of the parity operator. The first part of the definition implies that these fields (both potentials and field strengths) are irreducible tensors of rank L. There will be two kinds of 2^L pole fields, one with even parity and one with odd parity. The field for which

$$\Pi\mathbf{H} = (-)^L\mathbf{H} \tag{2.34}$$

is defined as the *electric* multipole field, and that for which

$$\Pi\mathbf{H} = (-)^{L+1}\mathbf{H} \tag{2.35}$$

is defined as the *magnetic* multipole field. These latter statements imply that $\mathbf{H} \neq 0$ so that the longitudinal field is automatically excluded.

As noted previously, the general solution of the scalar Helmholtz equation is a linear combination of the set $F_\lambda(kr)\ Y_\lambda^m(\mathbf{r})$, where $\sqrt{x}\ F_\lambda(x)$ is a cylinder function. Considering one member of the set, that is, a particular value of λ, the transformation properties under rotation are unaffected by the (scalar) radial function and only the spherical harmonic need be considered. Obviously Y_λ is an irreducible tensor of rank λ.

For the vector Helmholtz equation, which the vector potential $\mathbf{A}$ satisfies, we must construct a set of three solutions with the correct transformation properties. In order to do this we introduce the spherical basis vectors

$$\boldsymbol{\xi}_{\pm 1} = \mp \frac{1}{\sqrt{2}}(\mathbf{e}_x \pm i\mathbf{e}_y)$$

$$\boldsymbol{\xi}_0 = \mathbf{e}_z \tag{2.36}$$

where $\mathbf{e}_x$, $\mathbf{e}_y$, $\mathbf{e}_z$ are unit vectors along the cartesian coordinate axes. The motivation for this step is clear from the results of sec. 7. In fact,

[7] Parity requirements may exist, for example, $\pi_L = \pi_{L_1}\pi_{L_2}$ and only every other tensor rank is present. Equation 2.32 illustrates such a case.

we adopt a notation corresponding to (2.36) for all vectors and vector operators **B**:

$$B_{\pm 1} = \mp \frac{1}{\sqrt{2}}(B_x \pm iB_y) \qquad B_0 = B_z \tag{2.36$'$}$$

and in the following the components of the vector in the spherical basis will be used exclusively. For any vector **B**,

$$\mathbf{B} = \sum_\mu (-)^\mu B_\mu \boldsymbol{\xi}_{-\mu} \tag{2.37}$$

Since

$$\boldsymbol{\xi}_\mu^* = (-)^\mu \boldsymbol{\xi}_{-\mu} \tag{2.36$''$}$$

and

$$\boldsymbol{\xi}_\mu \cdot \boldsymbol{\xi}_{\mu'}^* = (-)^\mu \boldsymbol{\xi}_\mu \cdot \boldsymbol{\xi}_{-\mu'} = \delta_{\mu\mu'} \tag{2.38}$$

the spherical components of **B** are

$$B_\mu = \boldsymbol{\xi}_\mu \cdot \mathbf{B} = \mathbf{B} \cdot \boldsymbol{\xi}_\mu \tag{2.39}$$

We now consider an arbitrary vector field **A**(**r**) and show that under rotations wherein the vector transforms according to

$$\mathbf{A}' = e^{i\mathbf{n}\cdot\mathbf{J}\theta}\,\mathbf{A} \tag{2.40}$$

the angular-momentum operator **J** is given by

$$\mathbf{J} = \mathbf{L} + \mathbf{S}$$

and the components of S are just those given in (2.5).[8] Then the fact that the vectors $\boldsymbol{\xi}_\mu$ are the eigenfunctions of $\mathbf{S}^2$ and S_z will permit us to construct the desired multipole fields. In order to establish the connection with the previous notation we use cartesian coordinates in the first step of this development.

We begin with a rotation through an angle θ about the z-axis. Then if x, y, z, or, collectively, **r**, denote the coordinates of a point in the rotated coordinate system, and $\tau_z^{-1}\mathbf{r}$ the coordinates of this point in the original coordinate system, we have

$$\mathbf{A}'(\mathbf{r}) = \tau_z \mathbf{A}(\tau_z^{-1}\mathbf{r}) \tag{2.40$'$}$$

where

$$\tau_z = \begin{pmatrix} \cos\theta & \sin\theta & 0 \\ -\sin\theta & \cos\theta & 0 \\ 0 & 0 & 1 \end{pmatrix}$$

[8] As was mentioned above, equation 2.23 or the equivalent, equation 2.40, may be taken as the definition of the angular-momentum operator, and, from an investigation of the transformation properties, the explicit definition of **J** in each particular case is obtained. This is the procedure followed in this section. From the explicit representation of **J** the commutation rules (2.1) follow.

and the inverse matrix is

$$\tau_z^{-1} = \begin{pmatrix} \cos\theta & -\sin\theta & 0 \\ \sin\theta & \cos\theta & 0 \\ 0 & 0 & 1 \end{pmatrix}$$

In detailed form (2.40′) is

$$A_x'(\mathbf{r}) = \cos\theta\, A_x\,(x\cos\theta - y\sin\theta,\, y\cos\theta + x\sin\theta,\, z)$$
$$+ \sin\theta\, A_y(x\cos\theta - y\sin\theta,\, y\cos\theta + x\sin\theta,\, z) \quad (2.41a)$$
$$A_y'(\mathbf{r}) = -\sin\theta\, A_x(x\cos\theta - y\sin\theta,\, y\cos\theta + x\sin\theta,\, z)$$
$$+ \cos\theta\, A_y(x\cos\theta - y\sin\theta,\, y\cos\theta + x\sin\theta,\, z) \quad (2.41b)$$
$$A_z'(\mathbf{r}) = A_z(x\cos\theta - y\sin\theta,\, y\cos\theta + x\sin\theta,\, z) \quad (2.41c)$$

It is sufficient to consider an infinitesimal rotation. With the replacement of $\sin\theta$ by θ, $\cos\theta$ by 1, a Taylor expansion gives

$$\mathbf{A}' - \mathbf{A} = i\theta J_z \mathbf{A}$$

where

$$J_z = -i\left(x\frac{\partial}{\partial y} - y\frac{\partial}{\partial x}\right) + \begin{pmatrix} 0 & -i & 0 \\ i & 0 & 0 \\ 0 & 0 & 0 \end{pmatrix}$$
$$= L_z + S_z$$

by (2.3) and (2.5).[9]

By cyclically permuting the x, y, and z coordinates the corresponding results for a rotation around the x- and y-axes are obtained. The x- and y-components of the intrinsic angular-momentum operator $\mathbf{S}$ are just the matrices S_x and S_y of (2.5). It may be observed that the representation (2.5) is not the same as that defined by (2.9) and (2.14). If we designate the latter representation by $\mathbf{M}$, the two representations differ by a unitary transformation:

$$U\mathbf{S}U^{-1} = \mathbf{M}$$

where

$$U = \frac{1}{\sqrt{2}}\begin{pmatrix} 1 & -i & 0 \\ 0 & 0 & -\sqrt{2} \\ -1 & -i & 0 \end{pmatrix}$$

[9] We note incidentally that for a scalar field $\psi(\mathbf{r})$, an example of which is the set of functions Y_L^M, the transformation replacing (2.40′) is $\psi'(\tau_z\mathbf{r}) = \psi(\mathbf{r})$ or $\psi'(\mathbf{r}) = \psi(\tau_z^{-1}\mathbf{r})$. Then $J_z = L_z$ (i.e., $S = 0$) and $\mathbf{J} = \mathbf{L}$.

which corresponds to the change from the cartesian to the spherical basis.[10]

In the light of these results the rotated field is

$$\mathbf{A}' = \mathbf{A} + i\theta\mathbf{n}\cdot\mathbf{J}\,\mathbf{A}$$

with

$$\mathbf{J} = \mathbf{L} + \mathbf{S}$$

for a rotation about the direction **n**.

By direct multiplication it is seen that

$$\mathbf{S} \times \mathbf{S} = i\mathbf{S}$$

and

$$\mathbf{S}^2 = 2\begin{pmatrix} 1 & 0 & 0 \\ 0 & 1 & 0 \\ 0 & 0 & 1 \end{pmatrix}$$

or **S** is an angular-momentum operator with the eigenvalue of $\mathbf{S}^2 = s(s+1)$ with $s = 1$. Since

$$S_z\begin{pmatrix} A_x \\ A_y \\ A_z \end{pmatrix} = -i\begin{pmatrix} A_y \\ -A_x \\ 0 \end{pmatrix}$$

it follows that

$$S_z\,\boldsymbol{\xi}_\mu = \mu\,\boldsymbol{\xi}_\mu \tag{2.42}$$

In fact, it can be seen that

$$S_\sigma\,\boldsymbol{\xi}_\mu = (-)^\sigma\sqrt{2}\,C(111;\mu+\sigma,\,-\sigma)\,\boldsymbol{\xi}_{\mu+\sigma} \tag{2.42$'$}$$

This is a special case of the general result

$$J_\sigma\,\psi_j^m = (-)^\sigma\sqrt{j(j+1)}\,C(j1j;m+\sigma,\,-\sigma)\,\psi_j^{m+\sigma} \tag{2.42$''$}$$

which follows from (2.9), (2.14), and Table I.

From these results it follows that the $\boldsymbol{\xi}_\mu$ are the angular-momentum eigenfunctions in the space of the basis vectors and correspond to "spin" 1. On the other hand the spherical harmonics $Y_\lambda(\mathbf{r})$ are the angular-momentum wave functions in the space of the unit vector **r**. It follows that

$$\mathbf{T}_{L\lambda}^M \equiv \sum_\mu C(1\lambda L;\,-\mu,\,M+\mu)\,Y_\lambda^{M+\mu}(\mathbf{r})\,\boldsymbol{\xi}_{-\mu} \tag{2.43}$$

are (*a*) the angular-momentum eigenfunctions in the compound space

[10] If the change of basis is denoted by $\boldsymbol{\xi} = C\mathbf{e}$ then $\pm C = U^{-1} = U^+$. Comparison with (2.36) shows that the minus sign applies.

$$Y_\lambda^{M+\mu}\,\vec{\xi}_{-\mu} = \sum_{LM}\vec{T}_{L\lambda}^{M}\,C(1\lambda L;\,-\mu,\,M+\mu)$$

and (*b*) irreducible tensors of rank L, parity $(-)^\lambda$. It also follows immediately that

$$\mathbf{J}^2\, \mathbf{T}_{L\lambda}^M = L(L+1)\, \mathbf{T}_{L\lambda}^M \tag{2.44a}$$

$$J_z\, \mathbf{T}_{L\lambda}^M = M\, \mathbf{T}_{L\lambda}^M \tag{2.44b}$$

Finally, the triangular condition $\Delta(1\lambda L)$ implies that there are three linearly independent irreducible tensors of rank L. These are $\mathbf{T}_{L,L\pm1}^M$ and $\mathbf{T}_{LL}^M$.[11] Since these tensors span a three-dimensional space it is evident that for given L, M they form a complete set. This means that any vector field on the unit sphere can be expanded in terms of these tensors.

The tensors $\mathbf{T}_{L\lambda}^M$, which have been referred to as "vectorial spherical harmonics" [Blatt and Weisskopf (52)], actually transform with D^L and not, in general, with D^1. The term "vector," as used here, does not imply transformation with D^1 and is therefore not equivalent to a first-rank tensor. As used in the foregoing a vector is actually an invariant under rotation. A special case is $\mathbf{T}_{01}^0$ which is proportional to $\mathbf{r}$.[11] In fact, from (2.20*c*) and (2.21′)

$$C(110; -\mu, \mu+M) = -\frac{1}{\sqrt{3}}(-)^\mu \delta_{MO}$$

and it is seen from (2.37) that while the components of a vector, B_μ, and the $\boldsymbol{\xi}_\mu$ transform with D^1, the vector $\mathbf{B}$ itself transforms with D^0. Thus, the components B_μ and the base vectors $\boldsymbol{\xi}_\mu$ transform cogrediently, and

$$\mathbf{B} = \sum_\mu (-)^\mu B_\mu\, \boldsymbol{\xi}_{-\mu} = \sum_\mu (-)^\mu B'_\mu\, \boldsymbol{\xi}'_{-\mu}$$

This is in complete accord with equation 2.40, which is actually a relation between *components* of the vector as (2.41) shows explicitly.

The properties of the irreducible tensors introduced in (2.43) will be further discussed in Chapter III.

10. CONSTRUCTION OF THE MULTIPOLE FIELDS

All that is needed to construct a solution of the vector Helmholtz equation for the vector potential is to adjoin the appropriate radial function f_λ or g_λ to the tensor $\mathbf{T}_{L\lambda}^M$. We use the symbol ζ_λ to denote the general radial function. In order that the solutions be eigenfunctions of the parity operator we may mix $\mathbf{T}_{L,L+1}$ and $\mathbf{T}_{L,L-1}$, but $\mathbf{T}_{L,L}$,

[11] In the case $L = 0$, there is only one tensor (scalar) since the only possible resultant with angular-momentum vectors 0 and 1 is 1. Thus, for $L = 0$ only $\mathbf{T}_{01}^0 = -(4\pi)^{-1/2}\mathbf{r}$ is different from zero.

having the opposite parity, cannot be mixed with these. It follows from (2.34) and (2.35) that

$$\mathbf{A}_L^M(m) = c_L\, \zeta_L(kr)\, \mathbf{T}_{LL}^M \tag{2.45}$$

is the vector potential of the magnetic 2^L pole field and that

$$\mathbf{A}_L^M(e) = \sum_\lambda c_\lambda\, \zeta_\lambda(kr)\, \mathbf{T}_{L\lambda}^M \qquad \lambda = L \pm 1 \tag{2.46}$$

is the vector potential of the electric 2^L pole field.[12] The c_λ are coefficients which will be discussed below. Both of these are irreducible tensors of rank L (transform with D^L) and are therefore eigenfunctions of $\mathbf{J}^2$ and J_z with eigenvalues $L(L+1)$ and M respectively. $\mathbf{A}_L^M(m)$ has parity $(-)^L$, whereas $\mathbf{A}_L^M(e)$ has parity $(-)^{L-1}$. Thus, $\mathbf{H}(m)$ and $\mathbf{H}(e)$ have the required parity properties: $(-)^{L-1}$ and $(-)^L$, respectively.

The constant c_L in (2.45) is, of course, a normalization constant. The two constants c_{L-1} and c_{L+1} in (2.46) are equivalent to a normalization constant $(c_{L-1}^2 + c_{L+1}^2)^{1/2}$ and a second constant c_{L-1}/c_{L+1} which is fixed by the gauge. As will be shown in sec. 12, the magnetic vector potential, as given by (2.45), is already in the solenoidal gauge. The electric vector potential (2.46) is in an arbitrary gauge.

11. THE GRADIENT FORMULA AND THE RACAH COEFFICIENTS

Subsequent developments are greatly facilitated by the use of the gradient formula which gives the gradient of a function F of the space coordinates in the form $F = \Phi(r)\, Y_L^M(\mathbf{r})$. The result to be obtained gives a direct expression of the longitudinal field, and we are thereby enabled to express the gauge transformation in terms of the irreducible tensors $\mathbf{T}_{L\lambda}^M$.

Using the identity

$$\nabla = \mathbf{r}(\mathbf{r}\cdot\nabla) - \mathbf{r} \times (\mathbf{r} \times \nabla) \tag{2.47}$$

we write

$$\nabla\Phi(r)\, Y_L^M \equiv \mathbf{B} = \mathbf{B}_1 + \mathbf{B}_2$$

where the radial part, $\mathbf{B}_1$, commutes with any function of angular variables alone, and the tangential part, $\mathbf{B}_2$, commutes with any radial function. Here

$$\mathbf{B}_1 = \mathbf{r}\, Y_L^M \frac{d\Phi}{dr}$$

[12] An exception occurs for $c_{L-1}/c_{L+1} = \sqrt{L/L+1}$; cf. equation 2.65 below. This case corresponds to the longitudinal field for which the Poynting flux vanishes.

and

$$\mathbf{B}_2 = -\Phi\,\mathbf{r} \times (\mathbf{r} \times \nabla) Y_L^M$$

With the aid of

$$\boldsymbol{\xi}_\mu \cdot \mathbf{r} = \mathrm{r}_\mu = \sqrt{\frac{4\pi}{3}}\, Y_1^\mu(\mathbf{r})$$

and (2.32) we find for the μth component of $\mathbf{B}_1$

$$\mathbf{B}_1 \cdot \boldsymbol{\xi}_\mu = \frac{d\Phi}{dr}\left\{\sqrt{\frac{L+1}{2L+3}}\, C(L1\,L{+}1;\, M\mu)\, Y_{L+1}^{M+\mu} - \sqrt{\frac{L}{2L-1}}\, C(L1\,L{-}1;\, M\mu)\, Y_{L-1}^{M+\mu}\right\} \tag{2.48}$$

To evaluate $\mathbf{B}_2$ we first observe from (2.3) that

$$\mathbf{B}_2 = -\frac{i\Phi}{r}\,\mathbf{r} \times \mathbf{L} Y_L^M \tag{2.49}$$

and from (2.14) and Table I it follows that

$$L_\sigma Y_L^M = (-)^\sigma \sqrt{L(L+1)}\, C(L1L;\, M{+}\sigma,\, -\sigma)\, Y_L^{M+\sigma} \tag{2.50}$$

Hence

$$\begin{aligned}\mathbf{B}_2 \cdot \boldsymbol{\xi}_\mu &= -\frac{i\Phi}{r}(\boldsymbol{\xi}_\mu \times \mathbf{r}) \cdot \mathbf{L} Y_L^M \\ &= \sqrt{\frac{8\pi L(L+1)}{3}}\,\frac{\Phi}{r} \sum_{\sigma\nu} C(L1L;\, M{+}\sigma,\, -\sigma)\, C(111;\, \mu{-}\nu,\, \nu) \\ &\qquad \times Y_1^\nu\, Y_L^{M+\sigma}\, \boldsymbol{\xi}_{\mu-\nu} \cdot \boldsymbol{\xi}_{-\sigma}\end{aligned}$$

wherein

$$\boldsymbol{\xi}_\mu \times \mathbf{r} = i\sqrt{\frac{8\pi}{3}} \sum_\nu C(111;\, \mu{-}\nu,\, \nu)\, Y_1^\nu\, \boldsymbol{\xi}_{\mu-\nu} = i\sqrt{\frac{8\pi}{3}}\, \mathbf{T}_{11}^\mu \tag{2.51}$$

has been used. The result (2.51) is most readily derived by inspection, see Table I. Using (2.32) and (2.38) we obtain

$$\mathbf{B}_2 \cdot \boldsymbol{\xi}_\mu = \sqrt{2L(L+1)(2L+1)}\,\frac{\Phi}{r} \sum_\lambda \frac{C(L1\lambda;\, 00)}{\sqrt{2\lambda+1}}\, Y_\lambda^{M+\mu}\, \mathcal{S} \tag{2.52}$$

where $\mathcal{S}$ is the sum

$$\mathcal{S} = \sum_\sigma (-)^\sigma\, C(111;\, \sigma,\, \mu{-}\sigma)\, C(L1L;\, M{+}\sigma,\, -\sigma)\, C(L1\lambda;\, M{+}\sigma,\, \mu{-}\sigma) \tag{2.52a}$$

Sums over projection quantum numbers of products of three (or more) C-coefficients can be carried out using techniques developed by Racah (42) and (43). The results are invariably expressed in terms of Racah (W) coefficients, which are, within a normalization constant, the elements of a unitary matrix connecting two representations in the coupling of three angular momenta. Thus, consider the case of three angular momenta $\mathbf{j}_1$, $\mathbf{j}_2$, and $\mathbf{j}_3$ with projection quantum numbers m_1, m_2, and m_3 respectively, and the coupling of these to yield an eigenfunction of the total (square) angular momentum and projection operator with eigenvalues $J(J+1)$ and M. One representation is obtained by the coupling scheme

$$\mathbf{j}_1 + \mathbf{j}_2 = \mathbf{j}'$$

$$\mathbf{j}' + \mathbf{j}_3 = \mathbf{J}$$

and another by the coupling scheme

$$\mathbf{j}_2 + \mathbf{j}_3 = \mathbf{j}''$$

$$\mathbf{j}'' + \mathbf{j}_1 = \mathbf{J}$$

The unitary transformation which effects the recoupling from the first to the second transformation (coupling schemes) is

$$(j_1j_2(j')j_3J\,|\,j_1, j_2j_3(j''), J) \equiv \sqrt{(2j'+1)(2j''+1)}\; W(j_1j_2Jj_3; j'j'')$$
$$= \sum C(j'j_3J; m'm_3)\, C(j_1j_2j'; m_1m_2)\, C(j_2j_3j''; m_2m_3)\, C(j_1j''J; m_1m'') \tag{2.53}$$

and the summation is over m_1, m_2, m_3, m', m'' with

$$m_1 + m_2 + m_3 = M$$

$$m_1 + m_2 = m'$$

$$m_2 + m_3 = m''$$

From (2.53) it is clear that $W(abcd; ef)$ is different from zero only if the triangular conditions $\Delta(abe)$, $\Delta(cde)$, $\Delta(acf)$, $\Delta(bdf)$ are fulfilled. Using the unitary properties of the C-coefficients, (2.17) and (2.18), we deduce from (2.53) the very useful result:

$$C(j_1j_2j; m_1m_2)\, C(jj_3j_4; m_1{+}m_2, m_3) = \sum_s \sqrt{(2s+1)(2j+1)}$$
$$\times\, C(j_2j_3s; m_2m_3)\, C(j_1sj_4; m_1, m_2{+}m_3)\, W(j_1j_2j_4j_3; js) \tag{2.54}$$

Equation 2.54 is the form generally used for evaluating sums like (2.52a) in terms of Racah coefficients. Numerical values of these coefficients have been given by Biedenharn (51), and the properties of the W-coefficients have been summarized by Biedenharn, Blatt, and Rose (52).[13] In general, the procedure for evaluating the sums of products of C-coefficients is to note that in a given pair of C-coefficients one of the three projection quantum numbers (either one of the two which appear explicitly, or their sum) in each C-coefficient is independent of the summation index. By means of the symmetry relations (2.20) this projection quantum number can be brought into the second place, that is, into the position of m_2 as it appears on the left-hand side of (2.20). Then, when (2.54) is applied, one of the C-coefficients appearing on the right-hand side (namely, the first) will be independent of the summation index. Repeated application of this procedure will eventually reduce the sum to the form (2.17). The result is to introduce a number of Racah coefficients (W) equal to the number of Racah recouplings (2.54). Further transformation of the results is effected by the symmetry relations

$$\begin{aligned} W(abcd; ef) &= W(badc; ef) = W(cdab; ef) \\ &= W(acbd; fe) = (-)^{e+f-a-d} W(ebcf; ad) \\ &= (-)^{e+f-b-c} W(aefd; bc) \end{aligned} \tag{2.55}$$

or combinations of these permutations of the arguments.

These symmetry relations may be visualized geometrically by constructing a quadrilateral. For example, for $W(abcd; ef)$ the sides a and d are opposite, as are c and b. The diagonals are e and f so chosen that $\Delta(abe)$ and $\Delta(acf)$ pertain. Any permutation which preserves the triangular relations is permissible, and permutations of the sides (or diagonals) among themselves introduce no phase factor. Permutations in which sides and diagonals are transposed introduce a phase. Thus, transposition of the diagonal e and the side b introduces $(-)^{b-e}$. Such transpositions always occur in pairs (that is, both diagonals are replaced by sides) so that the exponent in the phase factor is an integer in every case.

It is also useful to note that

$$W(abcd; 0f) = (-)^{b+c-f} \frac{\delta_{ab}\,\delta_{cd}}{\sqrt{(2b+1)(2c+1)}} \tag{2.55'}$$

by (2.53), and by (2.55) the Racah coefficient can be brought to this form whenever any one of the six parameters vanishes.

[13] Cf. Appendix B. See also Sharp et al. (53).

In the manner indicated above we find

$$\mathcal{S} = \sqrt{3(2L+1)}\, C(L1\lambda; M\mu)\, W(L1\lambda 1; L1) \tag{2.56}$$

which, when substituted in (2.52), yields

$$\begin{aligned} \mathbf{B}_2 \cdot \boldsymbol{\xi}_\mu = (2L+1)\sqrt{6L(L+1)}\,\frac{\Phi}{r} \\ \times \left\{ \frac{C(L1\,L{+}1; 00)}{\sqrt{2L+3}} C(L1\,L{+}1; M\mu)\, W(L1\,L{+}1\,1; L1)\, Y_{L+1}^{M+\mu} \right. \\ \left. + \frac{C(L1\,L{-}1; 00)}{\sqrt{2L-1}} C(L1\,L{-}1; M\mu)\, W(L1\,L{-}1\,1; L1)\, Y_{L-1}^{M+\mu} \right\} \end{aligned}$$

From Tables I and BII of Appendix B we have

$$C(L1\,L{+}1; 00) = \sqrt{\frac{L+1}{2L+1}}; \qquad C(L1\,L{-}1; 00) = -\sqrt{\frac{L}{2L+1}} \tag{2.56a}$$

$$W(L1\,L{+}1\,1; L1) = W(L\,L{+}1\,11; 1L) = -\sqrt{\frac{L}{6(L+1)(2L+1)}} \tag{2.56b}$$

$$W(L1\,L{-}1\,1; L1) = W(L\,L{-}1\,11; 1L) = \sqrt{\frac{L+1}{6L(2L+1)}} \tag{2.56c}$$

Finally,

$$\begin{aligned} \mathbf{B} \cdot \boldsymbol{\xi}_\mu = \nabla_\mu\, \Phi(r)\, Y_L^M = \sqrt{\frac{L+1}{2L+3}}\, C(L1\,L{+}1; M\mu)\, Y_{L+1}^{M+\mu} \left(\frac{d\Phi}{dr} - \frac{L}{r}\Phi \right) \\ - \sqrt{\frac{L}{2L-1}}\, C(L1\,L{-}1; M\mu)\, Y_{L-1}^{M+\mu} \left(\frac{d\Phi}{dr} + \frac{L+1}{r}\Phi \right) \end{aligned} \tag{2.57}$$

This is the desired gradient formula. It can also be expressed in terms of the irreducible tensors as follows:

$$\begin{aligned} \nabla \Phi(r) Y_L^M = -\sqrt{\frac{L+1}{2L+1}} \left(\frac{d\Phi}{dr} - \frac{L}{r}\Phi \right) \mathbf{T}_{L,L+1}^M \\ + \sqrt{\frac{L}{2L+1}} \left(\frac{d\Phi}{dr} + \frac{L+1}{r}\Phi \right) \mathbf{T}_{L,L-1}^M \end{aligned} \tag{2.58}$$

It is clear that (2.58) is the vector potential of a 2^L pole longitudinal field when $\Phi(r)$ is a spherical bessel or hankel function.

12. THE SOLENOIDAL GAUGE

The result (2.58) can be used immediately to investigate the solenoidal gauge. We consider

$$\begin{aligned} \operatorname{div} \zeta_\lambda \mathbf{T}_{L\lambda}^M &= \sum_\mu (-)^\mu \nabla_\mu \zeta_\lambda \mathbf{T}_{L\lambda}^M \cdot \boldsymbol{\xi}_{-\mu} \\ &= \sum_\mu C(1\lambda L; \mu, M-\mu) \nabla_\mu Y_\lambda^{M-\mu} \zeta_\lambda \end{aligned} \tag{2.59}$$

where (2.38) and (2.43) have been used. By (2.58) and the orthogonality rule (2.17) this becomes

$$\begin{aligned} \operatorname{div} \zeta_\lambda \mathbf{T}_{L\lambda}^M &= \sqrt{\frac{\lambda+1}{2\lambda+3}}\, \delta_{L\lambda+1}\, Y_{\lambda+1}^M \left(\frac{d\zeta_\lambda}{dr} - \frac{\lambda}{r}\zeta_\lambda\right) \\ &\quad - \sqrt{\frac{\lambda}{2\lambda-1}}\, \delta_{L\lambda-1}\, Y_{\lambda-1}^M \left(\frac{d\zeta_\lambda}{dr} + \frac{\lambda+1}{r}\zeta_\lambda\right) \\ &= -\left\{\sqrt{\frac{L+1}{2L+1}}\, \delta_{\lambda L+1} + \sqrt{\frac{L}{2L+1}}\, \delta_{\lambda L-1}\right\} kY_L^M \zeta_L \end{aligned} \tag{2.60}$$

Here we have used

$$\frac{d\zeta_\lambda}{dx} = \frac{\lambda}{x}\zeta_\lambda - \zeta_{\lambda+1} = -\frac{\lambda+1}{x}\zeta_\lambda + \zeta_{\lambda-1} \tag{2.60'}$$

where $x = kr$.

This result makes it obvious that the magnetic multipole field, (2.45), is already in the solenoidal gauge. For the electric multipole field (2.46) shows that the solenoidal gauge corresponds to

$$c_{L-1}/c_{L+1} = -\sqrt{(L+1)/L} \tag{2.61}$$

We choose the normalization

$$c_L = -1 \qquad c_{L+1} = -\sqrt{L/(2L+1)} \tag{2.62}$$

so that $c_{L+1}^2 + c_{L-1}^2 = 1$. The choice (2.62) will be shown in sec. 15 to be equivalent to normalization to the same Poynting flux so that the electric and magnetic multipoles will be dual fields. Obviously, this statement applies to any gauge. With the normalization (2.62) the vector potentials in the solenoidal gauge are

$$\mathbf{A}_L^M(m) = -\zeta_L \mathbf{T}_{LL}^M \tag{2.63}$$

$$\mathbf{A}_L^M(e) = -\sqrt{\frac{L}{2L+1}}\zeta_{L+1}\mathbf{T}_{L,L+1}^M + \sqrt{\frac{L+1}{2L+1}}\zeta_{L-1}\mathbf{T}_{L,L-1}^M \tag{2.64}$$

To these we add the longitudinal field

$$\mathbf{A}_L^M(l) = \frac{1}{k}\nabla\zeta_L Y_L^M$$

$$= \sqrt{\frac{L+1}{2L+1}}\zeta_{L+1}\mathbf{T}_{L,L+1}^M + \sqrt{\frac{L}{2L+1}}\zeta_{L-1}\mathbf{T}_{L,L-1}^M \tag{2.65}$$

and the three fields constitute a complete set. Only in the subspace of solenoidal vectors will the radiative fields given by (2.63) and (2.64) form a complete set. Corresponding to the vector potential $\mathbf{A}_L^M(l)$, the scalar potential is

$$U_L^M(l) = i\zeta_L Y_L^M \tag{2.66}$$

We note that the conjugate fields are given with the aid of

$$\mathbf{T}_{L\lambda}^{M*} = (-)^{1+L-\lambda+M}\mathbf{T}_{L\lambda}^{-M}$$

as follows directly from the definition (2.43).

We shall consider gauge transformations with a gauge function, see equation 1.24,

$$S = \frac{a}{k}\zeta_L Y_L^M \tag{2.67}$$

where a is an arbitrary constant. The gauge-transformed vector potential for the electric multipole field is then

$$\mathbf{A}_L'^M = \left\{\frac{a\sqrt{L+1} - \sqrt{L}}{\sqrt{2L+1}}\right\}\zeta_{L+1}\mathbf{T}_{L,L+1}^M + \left\{\frac{a\sqrt{L} + \sqrt{L+1}}{\sqrt{2L+1}}\right\}\zeta_{L-1}\mathbf{T}_{L,L-1}^M \tag{2.68}$$

When $\zeta_L = g_L$ (outgoing wave) it is very convenient to use the so-called *conventional* gauge which corresponds to the choice

$$a = \sqrt{L/(L+1)}$$

Thus, the conventional gauge is that for which the most singular term (involving g_{L+1}) vanishes. In this gauge the potentials are

$$\mathbf{A}' = \sqrt{\frac{2L+1}{L+1}}\, \zeta_{L-1}\, \mathbf{T}^{M}_{L,L-1} \tag{2.69}$$

and

$$U' = i\sqrt{\frac{L}{L+1}}\, \zeta_L\, Y_L^M \tag{2.70}$$

The application of these results to internal conversion of atomic electrons will be given in Chapter V.

13. STATIC INTERACTIONS

As an illustration of some of the ideas presented in preceding sections we consider two simple physical applications. This will constitute a digression from the main consideration of dynamic multipole fields but will serve to introduce some useful concepts.

The first application to be treated is the elementary one of a configuration of static charges arranged in such a way that no lower moments than the 2^L pole moment exists. Then there are 2^L charges, half of them positive and half negative. The electrostatic potential is

$$V_L = \sqrt{4\pi}\, e(-)^L \prod_{n=1}^{L} (\mathbf{a}_n \cdot \nabla)\Upsilon_0^0 \tag{2.71}$$

where e is the absolute value of each charge and

$$\Upsilon_L^M = r^{-L-1} Y_L^M(\mathbf{r})$$

is the irregular solid harmonic of degree L. The vectors $\mathbf{a}_1 \cdots \mathbf{a}_L$, which are L arbitrary constant vectors representing the charge distribution, commute in pairs. Using the gradient formula it is seen that only the first term contributes and

$$V_L = \sqrt{4\pi}\, e\left(\frac{4\pi}{3}\right)^{L/2} \sqrt{\frac{L!(2L-1)!!}{(2L+1)}} \sum_M (-)^M \mathfrak{I}_L^{-M}(\mathbf{a}_1 \cdots \mathbf{a}_L)\, \Upsilon_L^M(\mathbf{r}) \tag{2.72}$$

where

$$(2n+1)!! = 1\cdot 3\cdot 5 \cdots (2n+1)$$

and the tensors $\mathfrak{I}_L^M(\mathbf{a}_1 \cdots \mathbf{a}_L)$, which represent the multipole moments, are defined by the recurrence formula

$$\mathfrak{Z}_\lambda^M(\mathbf{a}_1 \cdots \mathbf{a}_\lambda) = \sum_\mu C(1\,\lambda-1\,\lambda;\, -\mu,\, M+\mu)\, \mathcal{Y}_1^{-\mu}(\mathbf{a}_\lambda)\, \mathfrak{Z}_{\lambda-1}^{M+\mu}(\mathbf{a}_1 \cdots \mathbf{a}_{\lambda-1}) \tag{2.73}$$

with

$$\mathfrak{Z}_1^M(\mathbf{a}_1) = \mathcal{Y}_1^M(\mathbf{a}_1) = \sqrt{\frac{3}{4\pi}}\, \mathbf{a}_1 \cdot \boldsymbol{\xi}_M$$

It is clear that the $\mathfrak{Z}_\lambda^M(\mathbf{a}_1 \cdots \mathbf{a}_\lambda)$ are irreducible tensors of rank λ, symmetric with respect to any permutation of the λ argument vectors. It is also to be noted that the form of (2.72) shows that the potential V_L is an invariant, as expected.

If $\mathbf{a}_1 = \mathbf{a}_2 = \cdots \mathbf{a}_L = \mathbf{r}'$ we find the standard result

$$V_L = \frac{4\pi e}{2L+1} L! \frac{r'^L}{r^{L+1}} \sum_M (-)^M Y_L^M(\mathbf{r})\, Y_L^{-M}(\mathbf{r}') = eL! \frac{r'^L}{r^{L+1}} P_L(\cos \Theta) \tag{2.74}$$

where Θ is the angle between $\mathbf{r}$ and $\mathbf{r}'$. For an arbitrary charge distribution with density ρ_0 the 2^L pole electric moments are proportional to

$$\int r'^L\, Y_L^M(\mathbf{r}')\, \rho_0(\mathbf{r}')\, d\mathbf{r}'$$

Cf. sec. 22.

As a second example we consider the interaction of an arbitrary spin I with an external field. The interaction of a nuclear spin with the field produced by surrounding orbital electrons is a case in point. For the purpose in hand we define a new irreducible tensor

$$\mathfrak{Z}_L^M(\mathbf{I}) = (\mathbf{I} \cdot \nabla)^L \mathcal{Y}_L^M(\mathbf{r}) \tag{2.75}$$

where $\mathcal{Y}_L^M = r^L Y_L^M(\mathbf{r})$ is the regular solid harmonic. It is to be noted that the components of $\mathbf{I}$ do not commute but instead $\mathbf{I} \times \mathbf{I} = i\mathbf{I}$ or, in terms of the spherical basis,

$$I_\mu I_\nu - I_\nu I_\mu = I_{\mu+\nu} \qquad \mu < \nu$$

Using (2.57) again, where now only the second term contributes, and defining the sequence of irreducible tensors $\mathfrak{Z}_{\lambda\lambda-1}^M(\mathbf{I})$ by

$$\mathfrak{Z}_{\lambda\lambda-1}^M(\mathbf{I}) = \sum_\mu C(1\,\lambda-1\,\lambda;\, -\mu,\, \mu+M)\, \mathfrak{Z}_{\lambda-1,\lambda-2}^{\mu+M}(\mathbf{I})\, \mathcal{Y}_1^{-\mu}(\mathbf{I}) \tag{2.75$'$}$$

with

$$\mathfrak{Z}_{10}^M(\mathbf{I}) = \mathcal{Y}_1^M(\mathbf{I}) \qquad \mathfrak{Z}_{0-1} = 0$$

we find that

$$\mathfrak{I}_L^M(\mathbf{I}) = \left(\frac{4\pi}{3}\right)^{L/2} \sqrt{\frac{L!(2L+1)!!}{4\pi}}\, \mathfrak{I}_{L,L-1}^M(\mathbf{I}) \tag{2.76}$$

For the interaction of two spin systems **I** and **J**, where **J** may represent the total angular momentum of the orbital electrons, the coupling energy is the invariant [14]

$$\mathfrak{H} = K \sum_M (-)^M \mathfrak{I}_L^M(\mathbf{I})\, \mathfrak{I}_L^{-M}(\mathbf{J}) \tag{2.77}$$

where K is a constant, see Casimir (36). For $L = 1$ the sum in (2.77) becomes $(3/4\pi)\mathbf{I}\cdot\mathbf{J}$, the usual cosine coupling of the hyperfine structure. For $L = 2$ the components of $\mathfrak{I}_2^M$ are given by

$$\mathfrak{I}_2^{\pm 2}(\mathbf{I}) = \sqrt{15/2\pi}\, I_{\pm 1}^2$$

$$\mathfrak{I}_2^{\pm 1}(\mathbf{I}) = \sqrt{15/4\pi}\, (I_0 I_{\pm 1} + I_{\pm 1} I_0)$$

$$\mathfrak{I}_2^{0}(\mathbf{I}) = \sqrt{5/4\pi}\, (3I_0^2 - \mathbf{I}^2)$$

and (2.77) yields the well-known quadrupole interaction. For a nuclear spin embedded in a crystalline lattice the expectation values of $\mathfrak{I}_2^{-M}(\mathbf{J})$ may be inserted in (2.77) in place of the corresponding tensor operators, and these parameters (the components of the electric field gradient tensor) are then treated as empirical constants, Pound (50). The matrix elements of the interaction (2.77) then depend on

$$(\Psi_I^{m_i} | \mathfrak{I}_L^M(\mathbf{I}) | \Psi_{I'}^{m_i'}) \equiv (Im_i | \mathfrak{I}_L^M(\mathbf{I}) | I'm_i') \tag{2.78}$$

where $\Psi_I^{m_i}$, etc., are the nuclear wave functions which diagonalize $\mathbf{I}^2$ and I_z.

The matrix elements (2.78) can be evaluated using the Eckart theorem [Eckart (30)], which gives the projection quantum number dependence of the matrix element of an irreducible tensor between angular-momentum eigenstates in the form of a C-coefficient. In the present case this takes the form:

$$(Im_i | \mathfrak{I}_L^M | I'm_i') = C(I'LI; m_i'M)(I \| \mathfrak{I}_L \| I') \tag{2.79}$$

where the second factor, the so-called reduced matrix element, is independent of the projection quantum numbers. The Eckart theorem, which is expressed quite generally by (2.79), is an immediate conse-

[14] Note that both $\mathfrak{I}_L^M(\mathbf{I})$ and $\mathfrak{I}_L^M(\mathbf{J})$ transform under D^L. With $C(LL0; M, -M) = (-)^{L-M}/\sqrt{2L+1}$ together with the use of the Clebsch-Gordan series (2.30), the invariance of (2.77) is readily demonstrated. This is simply a generalization of the invariant vector of sec. 9 where the contraction of two first-rank tensors is involved.

quence of the results of sec. 7; in particular, see equation 2.19, which applies here with $\psi_{j_1}^{m_1}$ replaced by $\mathfrak{Z}_L^M$, $\psi_{j_2}^{m_2}$ by $\Psi_{I'}^{m_i'}$, and $\psi_j^{m_1+m_2}$ by $\Psi_I^{m_i}$. A special case of the Eckart theorem has already been given in (2.33). In the present application the matrix elements are non-vanishing only for $I = I'$ since $\mathfrak{Z}_L^M(\mathbf{I})$ depends solely on the spin operator $\mathbf{I}$; cf. (2.09) and (2.14).

We need only evaluate the reduced matrix element, which can be done by considering a special case. Thus, from Wigner (31),

$$C(ILI; I-L, L) = (-)^L \sqrt{\frac{(2I+1)!(2L)!}{(2I+L+1)!L!}} \tag{2.80}$$

where we have taken $M = L$ and $m_i = I$. Then, in (2.75′) only $\mu = -1$ contributes, and by Table I

$$\mathfrak{Z}_{LL-1}^L = (\mathcal{Y}_1^1(\mathbf{I}))^L$$

From (2.14) we have

$$(Im|\mathcal{Y}_1^1(\mathbf{I})|I'm') = -\sqrt{(3/8\pi)(I-m_i')(I+m_i'+1)}\,\delta_{m_i,m_i'+1}\,\delta_{II'} \tag{2.80′}$$

By repeated use of (2.80′) we obtain

$$(Im_i|\mathfrak{Z}_L^M|I'm_i') = \delta_{m_i,m_i'+M}\,\delta_{II'}\,\frac{L!}{2^L} \times \sqrt{\frac{1}{4\pi}\frac{2L+1}{2I+1}\frac{(2I+L+1)!}{(2I-L)!}}\,C(ILI; m_i'M) \tag{2.81}$$

It is evident that for a given spin I multipole moments for $L \leq 2I$ only may exist. Thus, a quadrupole moment may exist only for $I \geq 1$.

From the formal point of view it may be noted that the two examples discussed in this section involve special cases of the process of "polarization." A general polarized solid harmonic is

$$\mathcal{Y}_L^M(\mathbf{a}_1\mathbf{a}_2 \cdots \mathbf{a}_L) = \prod_{n=1}^{L} (\mathbf{a}_n \cdot \nabla)\mathcal{Y}_L^M(\mathbf{r})$$

where the vectors $\mathbf{a}_1 \cdots \mathbf{a}_L$ are arbitrary and need not commute. When they do not commute the irreducible tensors defined by (2.75′), or an obvious extension thereof, provide automatically symmetrized polarized harmonics. For further details the reader is referred to Weyl (39), p. 149 et seq. These polarized harmonics, which are, of course, irreducible tensors, are also useful in the theory of angular correlation [Falkoff and Uhlenbeck (50)]. They may also be introduced advantageously in the theory of beta decay [Rose and Osborn (54)].

III. PROPERTIES OF THE MULTIPOLE FIELDS

14. ORTHOGONALITY OF THE FIELDS

The particular utility of the solenoidal gauge, discussed in sec. 12, lies in the fact that in this gauge the potentials $\mathbf{A}_L^M(\tau)$, with $\tau = m$, e, or l, form an orthogonal set. They also form a complete set, but, as will be evident, this is true for any gauge. To demonstrate the orthogonality we first consider the complete set of tensors $\mathbf{T}_{L\lambda}^M$ with $\lambda = L$, $L \pm 1$. Then on the unit sphere

$$\int \mathbf{T}_{L\lambda}^{M*} \cdot \mathbf{T}_{L'\lambda'}^{M'} \, d\Omega = \sum_{\mu\mu'} C(1\lambda L;\, -\mu,\, \mu+M)\; C(1\lambda' L';\, -\mu',\, \mu'+M') \times \boldsymbol{\xi}_{-\mu}^{*} \cdot \boldsymbol{\xi}_{-\mu'} \int d\Omega \; Y_{\lambda}^{M+\mu*} \; Y_{\lambda'}^{M'+\mu'}$$

where $d\Omega$ is the element of solid angle. Since $\boldsymbol{\xi}_{-\mu}^{*} \cdot \boldsymbol{\xi}_{-\mu'} = \delta_{\mu\mu'}$ and the angular integration yields $\delta_{\lambda\lambda'}\, \delta_{M+\mu,M'+\mu'}$ it follows that

$$\int \mathbf{T}_{L\lambda}^{M*} \cdot \mathbf{T}_{L'\lambda'}^{M'} \, d\Omega = \sum_{\mu} C(1\lambda L;\, -\mu,\, \mu+M)\; C(1\lambda' L';\, -\mu,\, \mu+M)\; \delta_{\lambda\lambda'}\, \delta_{MM'}$$

$$= \delta_{LL'}\, \delta_{\lambda\lambda'}\, \delta_{MM'} \tag{3.1}$$

From (2.63), (2.64), and (2.65) it follows that

$$\int d\Omega \; \mathbf{A}_L^{M*}(\tau) \cdot \mathbf{A}_{L'}^{M'}(\tau') = F(r)\, \delta_{LL'}\, \delta_{MM'}\, \delta_{\tau\tau'} \tag{3.2}$$

and

$$F(r) = |\zeta_L|^2 \qquad \text{for} \quad \tau = m$$

$$= \frac{L|\zeta_{L+1}|^2 + (L+1)|\zeta_{L-1}|^2}{2L+1} \qquad \tau = e$$

$$= \frac{(L+1)|\zeta_{L+1}|^2 + L|\zeta_{L-1}|^2}{2L+1} \qquad \tau = \tag{3.2'}$$

If we consider standing waves, $\zeta_L = f_L$, the normalization is given by

$$\int \mathbf{A}_L^{M*}(k\mathbf{r}) \cdot \mathbf{A}_L^M(k'\mathbf{r})\, d\mathbf{r} = \frac{1}{\sqrt{kk'}} \int_0^\infty r\, J_{L+\frac{1}{2}}(kr)\, J_{L+\frac{1}{2}}(k'r)\, dr$$

$$= (1/k^2)\, \delta(k - k') \tag{3.3}$$

for the magnetic multipoles. Since the radial integral in (3.3) is independent of L, the same result applies for electric and longitudinal fields.

If the gauge transformation (2.67) is carried out on the electric multipole field the transformed vector potential is no longer orthogonal to the longitudinal field but the magnetic multipole field remains orthogonal to both electric and longitudinal fields.

The completeness of the set $\mathbf{A}_L^M(\tau)$, ($\tau = m$, e, and l), follows from the completeness of the tensors $\mathbf{T}_{L\lambda}^M$, since $\mathbf{A}_L^M(e)$ and $\mathbf{A}_L^M(l)$ are two linearly independent combinations of $\mathbf{T}_{L\lambda}^M$, ($\lambda = L \pm 1$). A gauge transformation of $\mathbf{A}_L^M(e)$ corresponds to a rotation (and renormalization) of only the electric vector potential in the $\mathbf{T}_{L,L+1}^M - \mathbf{T}_{L,L-1}^M$ plane.

15. ALTERNATIVE FORMS OF THE MULTIPOLE POTENTIALS

Although the form (2.63)–(2.65) for the potentials in terms of irreducible tensors is the fundamental one from the point of view of identification of the transformation and angular-momentum properties, it is sometimes convenient to express the fields in other equivalent forms. Thus, from (2.50) and (2.63) it follows that

$$\mathbf{A}_L^M(m) = \zeta_L \frac{\mathbf{L}}{\sqrt{L(L+1)}}\, Y_L^M \tag{3.4}$$

Since $\mathbf{A}_L^M(m)$ is in the solenoidal gauge the field strengths are

$$\mathbf{E}_L^M(m) = ik\mathbf{A}_L^M(m) \tag{3.5}$$

and, with $\mathfrak{M} = 0$,

$$\mathbf{H}_L^M(m) = \text{curl } \mathbf{A}_L^M(m) \tag{3.6}$$

The dual field is

$$\mathbf{H}_L^M(e) = -\mathbf{E}_L^M(m) = -ik\mathbf{A}_L^M(m) \tag{3.7}$$

and

$$\mathbf{E}_L^M(e) = \mathbf{H}_L^M(m) = \text{curl } \mathbf{A}_L^M(m) \tag{3.8}$$

In the solenoidal gauge for the electric vector potential

$$\mathbf{E}_L^M(e) = ik\mathbf{A}_L^M(e)$$

and therefore

$$\mathbf{A}_L^M(e) = -\frac{1}{k\sqrt{L(L+1)}} \operatorname{curl} (\mathbf{r} \times \nabla)\zeta_L Y_L^M \tag{3.9}$$

The potentials as given by (3.4) and (3.9) were first obtained by Hansen (35); see also Stratton (41).

It follows from (3.4) and (3.9) that the magnetic and electric multipole fields vanish identically for $L = 0$.[1] In sec. 9 it has been shown that the only irreducible tensor of rank zero is proportional to the unit vector $\mathfrak{r}$. It is clear that the zero-rank tensor gives vanishing electric and magnetic field strengths and is a longitudinal field.

Using the identity

$$\operatorname{curl} (\mathbf{r} \times \nabla) = \mathbf{r}\nabla^2 - \nabla[1 + r(d/dr)] \tag{3.10}$$

the electric vector potential (3.9) becomes

$$\mathbf{A}_L^M(e) = \frac{1}{\sqrt{L(L+1)}} \left\{ k\mathbf{r}\, \zeta_L\, Y_L^M + \frac{1}{k} \nabla \left(1 + r\frac{d}{dr}\right) \zeta_L\, Y_L^M \right\} \tag{3.11}$$

Using (2.32) in conjunction with the first term and (2.58) with the second of (3.11), together with

$$\left\{ \frac{d^2}{dr^2} + \frac{2}{r}\frac{d}{dr} + k^2 - \frac{L(L+1)}{r^2} \right\} \zeta_L = 0$$

we find that (3.11) is identical with (2.64). This demonstrates that, with the normalization (2.62), the electric and magnetic multipole fields are dual fields. Hence the Poynting fluxes associated with these fields are the same.

The explicit forms for the electric and magnetic field strengths in terms of the irreducible tensors follows immediately:

$$\mathbf{E}_L^M(m) = -\mathbf{H}_L^M(e) = -ik\zeta_L \mathbf{T}_{LL}^M \tag{3.12}$$

$$\mathbf{H}_L^M(m) = \mathbf{E}_L^M(e)$$

$$= ik \left\{ -\sqrt{\frac{L}{2L+1}}\, \zeta_{L+1}\, \mathbf{T}_{L,L+1}^M + \sqrt{\frac{L+1}{2L+1}}\, \zeta_{L-1}\, \mathbf{T}_{L,L-1}^M \right\} \tag{3.13}$$

[1] This is obvious if we consider the fields without the normalization factor $1/\sqrt{L(L+1)}$. Then, since $L = 0$ need no longer be considered, the use of this normalization is permissible.

Obviously

$$\int d\Omega\, \mathbf{E}_L^M(m)\cdot\mathbf{H}_L^{M*}(m) = \int d\Omega\, \mathbf{E}_L^M(e)\cdot\mathbf{H}_L^{M*}(e)$$

$$= \int d\Omega\, \mathbf{E}_L^M(m)\cdot\mathbf{E}_L^{M*}(e)$$

$$= \int d\Omega\, \mathbf{H}_L^M(m)\cdot\mathbf{H}_L^{M*}(e) = 0$$

and the integration over the surface of the unit sphere vanishes for the scalar product of any field strength vector and the conjugate of any other multipole field strength ($L \neq L'$) or substate of the same multipole ($M \neq M'$).

16. RADIAL AND TANGENTIAL DECOMPOSITION OF THE FIELDS

For the discussion of the Poynting flux and the angular momentum of the fields it is convenient to decompose the field vectors into radial and tangential parts. Thus, for any vector **A**,

$$\mathbf{A} = \mathbf{A}_{\|} + \mathbf{A}_{\perp}$$

where $\mathbf{A}_{\|}$ is the radial part, parallel to $\mathfrak{r}$, and $\mathbf{A}_{\perp}$ is normal to $\mathfrak{r}$ and lies in the surface of a sphere. In general,

$$\mathbf{A}_{\|} = \mathfrak{r}(\mathbf{A}\cdot\mathfrak{r}) \tag{3.14a}$$

$$\mathbf{A}_{\perp} = -\mathfrak{r}\times(\mathfrak{r}\times\mathbf{A}) \tag{3.14b}$$

We consider the solenoidal gauge for the vector potential. Then

$$\mathbf{A}_{\|}(m) = 0 \qquad \mathbf{A}_{\perp}(m) = \mathbf{A}(m) \tag{3.15}$$

and, in any gauge,

$$\mathbf{E}_{\|}(m) = \mathbf{H}_{\|}(e) = 0 \tag{3.15a}$$

$$\mathbf{E}_{\perp}(m) = \mathbf{E}(m) \qquad \mathbf{H}_{\perp}(e) = \mathbf{H}(e) \tag{3.15b}$$

For convenience the indices L, M are omitted.

For the electric vector potential we use the form (3.9), writing it as

$$\mathbf{A}(e) = -\frac{1}{k\sqrt{L(L+1)}}\{\zeta_L \operatorname{curl}(\mathbf{r}\times\nabla)Y_L^M + \nabla\zeta_L\times(\mathbf{r}\times\nabla)Y_L^M\}$$

The first term in the brace is simplified by using (3.10):

$$\begin{aligned}\text{curl}\,(\mathbf{r}\times\nabla)Y_L^M &= \mathbf{r}\nabla^2 Y_L^M - \nabla[1 + r(d/dr)]Y_L^M \\ &= -(\mathbf{r}/r^2)L(L+1)Y_L^M - \nabla Y_L^M \qquad (3.16)\end{aligned}$$

Since $\nabla\zeta_L$ is in the direction $\mathbf{r}$ and ∇Y_L^M lies in the surface of the sphere, the first term on the right-hand side of (3.16) is the only contribution to $\mathbf{A}_{||}(e)$. Thus,

$$\mathbf{A}_{||}(e) = (1/k)\sqrt{L(L+1)}(\mathbf{r}/r)\zeta_L\, Y_L^M \qquad (3.17)$$

and

$$\mathbf{A}_{\perp}(e) = -\frac{1}{kr\sqrt{L(L+1)}}\left(1 + r\frac{d}{dr}\right)\zeta_L\,[\mathbf{r}\times(\mathbf{r}\times\nabla)Y_L^M] \qquad (3.18)$$

In terms of the irreducible tensors we find by the use of (2.20*a*), (2.20*b*), (2.20*c*), (2.21), and (2.56*a*) that

$$\begin{aligned}\mathbf{A}_{||}(e) &= -\sqrt{L(L+1)}\,\frac{\zeta_L}{kr}\left\{\sqrt{\frac{L+1}{2L+1}}\,\mathbf{T}_{L,L+1}^M - \sqrt{\frac{L}{2L+1}}\,\mathbf{T}_{L,L-1}^M\right\} \\ &= -\frac{\sqrt{L(L+1)}}{2L+1}(\zeta_{L+1} + \zeta_{L-1}) \\ &\quad\times\left\{\sqrt{\frac{L+1}{2L+1}}\,\mathbf{T}_{L,L+1}^M - \sqrt{\frac{L}{2L+1}}\,\mathbf{T}_{L,L-1}^M\right\} \qquad (3.19)\end{aligned}$$

by (2.60′).

For the field strengths

$$\mathbf{E}_{||}(e) = \mathbf{H}_{||}(m) = ik\mathbf{A}_{||}(e) \qquad (3.20)$$

It is also useful to note that

$$\begin{aligned}|\mathbf{r}\times(\mathbf{r}\times\nabla)Y_L^M|^2 &= |\mathbf{r}\times\mathbf{L}Y_L^M|^2 \\ &= \mathbf{r}\cdot\mathbf{L}Y_L^M \times (\mathbf{r}\times LY_L^M)^* \\ &= |\mathbf{L}Y_L^M|^2\end{aligned}$$

since the ∇ operator acts on Y_L^M only. Therefore

$$|\mathbf{A}_{\perp}(e)| = \frac{|\mathbf{L}Y_L^M|}{kr\sqrt{L(L+1)}}\left|\left(1 + r\frac{d}{dr}\right)\zeta_L\right| \qquad (3.21)$$

This may be compared with

$$|\mathbf{A}(m)| = \frac{|\mathbf{L}Y_L^M|}{\sqrt{L(L+1)}}|\zeta_L| \tag{3.22}$$

For $kr \gg 1$ it is seen that $|\mathbf{A}(e)| \cong |\mathbf{A}_\perp(e)| = |\mathbf{A}(m)|$ [cf. (3.24), below], and the same result applies for the field strengths.

17. POYNTING FLUX

To evaluate the Poynting flux we consider the outgoing wave field ($\zeta_L = g_L$) in the wave zone, that is, for $kr \gg 1$. The asymptotic behavior of g_L for large argument is

$$g_L \sim (-i)^{L+1}\sqrt{2/\pi}(e^{ikr}/kr) \tag{3.23}$$

so that $|g_L|$ is asymptotically independent of L. Also

$$[1 + r(d/dr)]g_L \sim ikrg_L \tag{3.24}$$

From the results of sec. 16 it is seen that $|\mathbf{A}_\perp(e)| \sim |g_L|$, apart from an angular dependent function and a constant, while $|\mathbf{A}_{||}(e)| \sim |g_L|/kr$. Hence, in the wave zone the perpendicular components dominate and the field is transverse for distances r large compared to the wavelength of the radiation.

From (1.32) the net energy flux is

$$P = \frac{cr^2}{2\pi}\int d\Omega\, \mathbf{r}\cdot\mathbf{E} \times \mathbf{H}^* \tag{3.25}$$

Since the flux P is the same for electric and magnetic multipoles we consider only the latter case. Then for a 2^L pole, omitting the L, M indices, we have

$$P = \frac{cr^2}{2\pi}\int d\Omega\, \mathbf{r}\cdot\mathbf{E}(m) \times \mathbf{H}^*(m)$$

$$= \frac{cr^2k^2}{2\pi}\int d\Omega\, \mathbf{r}\cdot\mathbf{A}(m) \times \mathbf{A}^*(e)$$

Using (3.4) for $\mathbf{A}(m)$ and (3.18) for $\mathbf{A}(e)$ we find

$$\mathbf{r}\cdot\mathbf{A}(m) \times \mathbf{A}^*(e) = \frac{ig_L\left(g_L + r\dfrac{dg_L}{dr}\right)^*}{krL(L+1)}\{\mathbf{r}\cdot\mathbf{L}Y_L^M \times (\mathbf{r} \times \mathbf{L}Y_L^M)^*\}$$

The factor in front of the brace is asymptotically

$$\frac{ig_L\left(g_L + r\dfrac{dg_L}{dr}\right)^*}{krL(L+1)} \sim \frac{|g_L|^2}{L(L+1)}$$

from (3.24). The factor in the braces is

$$\mathbf{r}\cdot\mathbf{L}Y_L^M \times (\mathbf{r}\times\mathbf{L}Y_L^M)^* = |\mathbf{L}Y_L^M|^2$$

From the hermitian property of the $\mathbf{L}$ operator we find

$$\int d\Omega\, |\mathbf{L}Y_L^M|^2 = \int d\Omega\, Y_L^{M*}\mathbf{L}^2 Y_L^M = L(L+1)$$

Hence, using (3.23)

$$P = c/\pi^2 \tag{3.26}$$

The number of quanta radiated per second is

$$P/\hbar\omega = 1/\pi^2\hbar k \tag{3.27}$$

Since $\mathbf{E}(m)\cdot\mathbf{H}^*(m) = \mathbf{E}_\perp(m)\cdot\mathbf{H}_\perp^*(m)$ and $\mathbf{E}_\perp(m)$ is proportional to $\mathbf{L}Y_L^M$ while, from (3.18), $\mathbf{H}_\perp(m)$ is in the direction $\mathbf{r}\times\mathbf{L}Y_L^M$, it follows that $\mathbf{E}(m)\cdot\mathbf{H}^*(m) = 0$ and, of course, the Poynting vector $\mathbf{N}$ is directed radially outward as was to be expected.

18. BEHAVIOR OF THE FIELDS IN THE STATIC ZONE

We consider the standing-wave solutions which are the only solutions regular at the origin. Then for $kr \ll 1$

$$\zeta_L = f_L \approx \sqrt{\frac{2}{\pi}}\frac{(kr)^L}{(2L+1)!!} \tag{3.28}$$

From the results of sec. 16 we find the following results for the dependence of the field strengths on kr in the static zone:

$$(1/k)\mathbf{E}_\perp(m) \sim (kr)^L \qquad (1/k)\mathbf{H}_\perp(m) \sim (kr)^{L-1}$$

$$(1/k)\mathbf{E}_\perp(e) \sim (kr)^{L-1} \qquad (1/k)\mathbf{H}_\perp(e) \sim (kr)^L$$

$$(1/k)\mathbf{E}_{||}(e) \sim (kr)^{L-1} \qquad (1/k)\mathbf{H}_{||}(m) \sim (kr)^{L-1}$$

It is seen that there is no distinction, so far as order of magnitude is concerned, between the radial and tangential components of the field strengths. This is apart from the components which vanish identically:

$\mathbf{E}_{||}(m) = \mathbf{H}_{||}(e) = 0$. However, for the magnetic multipole field

$$|\mathbf{H}(m)| \gg |\mathbf{E}(m)|$$

and for the electric multipole field

$$|\mathbf{E}(e)| \gg |\mathbf{H}(e)|$$

The nomenclature "electric" and "magnetic" multipole fields can be understood from this circumstance.

19. CLASSICAL DESCRIPTION OF THE ENERGY AND ANGULAR MOMENTUM

In the classical treatment of the electromagnetic field the total energy of the field is given by

$$W = \frac{1}{4\pi} \int (\mathbf{E}\cdot\mathbf{E}^* + \mathbf{H}\cdot\mathbf{H}^*)\, d\mathbf{r} \tag{3.29}$$

and the angular momentum is

$$\mathbf{G} = \frac{1}{4\pi c} \int \mathbf{r} \times (\mathbf{E} \times \mathbf{H}^* + \mathbf{E}^* \times \mathbf{H})\, d\mathbf{r} \tag{3.30}$$

It is again sufficient to consider only the magnetic multipole field since W and $\mathbf{G}$ are invariant under the dual transformation. The energy W becomes

$$\begin{aligned} W &= \frac{k^2}{4\pi} \int \{ |\mathbf{A}(m)|^2 + |\mathbf{A}(e)|^2 \}\, d\mathbf{r} \\ &= \frac{k^2}{4\pi} \int \left\{ f_L^2 + \frac{1}{2L+1} [L f_{L+1}^2 + (L+1) f_{L-1}^2] \right\} r^2\, dr \end{aligned}$$

where we have used (2.63), (2.64), and (3.1). Since the normalization of the radial functions is independent of L, see (3.3), this becomes

$$W = \frac{k^2}{2\pi} \int f_L^2\, r^2\, dr \tag{3.31}$$

Actually, the normalization previously used is not suitable for our present purpose. If the energy as given by (3.31) is to be equal to the energy of one quantum, viz., $W = \hbar\omega$, we must adopt the artifice of enclosing the field in a "box." The box may be taken to be a perfectly conducting sphere on the surface of which the tangential components of the electric field strength vanish. This boundary condition makes the k-spectrum discrete and permits a discrete set of eigenfunctions to exist. The normalization integral in (3.31) is then finite. If the volume of the box is V, the normalization integral is

$$\int f_L(k'r)\, f_L(k''r)\, r^2\, dr = V\, \delta_{k'k''}$$

where k' and k'' are two eigenvalues of the wave number, that is, roots of $f_L(kR) = 0$ where R is the radius of the spherical enclosure. Then, all the potentials may be renormalized by multiplication with the factor [2]

$$\eta = \sqrt{2\pi\hbar c^2/\omega V} \tag{3.32}$$

With this normalization

$$W = \hbar\omega$$

For the angular momentum we may write

$$\mathbf{G} = \eta^2 \int (\mathbf{g}' + \mathbf{g}'^*)\, d\mathbf{r}$$

where, for magnetic multipoles,

$$\begin{aligned} \mathbf{g}' &= (1/4\pi c)\mathbf{E}^*(\mathbf{H}\cdot\mathbf{r}) \\ &= (k^2/4\pi c)\mathbf{A}^*(m)[\mathbf{A}(e)\cdot\mathbf{r}] \end{aligned}$$

From (3.17)

$$\mathbf{A}(e)\cdot\mathbf{r} = \frac{\sqrt{L(L+1)}}{k} f_L\, Y_L^M$$

and, from (2.63)

$$\mathbf{g}' = -\frac{k}{4\pi c}\sqrt{L(L+1)}\, f_L^2\, Y_L^M \sum_\mu C(1LL; -\mu, M+\mu)\, (Y_L^{M+\mu})^* \boldsymbol{\xi}_{-\mu}^*$$

Consequently,

$$\begin{aligned} \mathbf{G} &= -\frac{k\eta^2}{2\pi c}\sqrt{L(L+1)} \sum_\mu C(1LL; -\mu, M+\mu)\, \boldsymbol{\xi}_{-\mu}^*\, \delta_{\mu 0} \int_0^\infty r^2 f_L^2\, dr \\ &= -\frac{k\eta^2}{2\pi c}\sqrt{L(L+1)}\, C(1LL; 0M)\, \boldsymbol{\xi}_0 \int_0^\infty r^2 f_L^2\, dr \end{aligned}$$

In other words,

$$\mathbf{G} = G_0 \boldsymbol{\xi}_0 \tag{3.33}$$

and only the z-component of the angular momentum is different from

[2] This represents one photon in the volume V in the quantized radiation field. See e.g., Wentzel (46).

zero. For this component we obtain from Table I, (2.20a), and (3.32),[3]

$$G_0 = M\hbar \tag{3.34}$$

From the results given in this section it is clear that the contribution to the angular momentum from various points r is the same as in the case of the energy. That is, the same radial integral is involved. It is also clear that the angular momentum, as well as the energy, receives contributions from all points and not just from the static zone; cf. Wallace (51), Blatt and Weisskopf (52).

These results are, of course, exactly the same as those given in a quantum-mechanical description. The vanishing of $G_{\pm 1}$ means, in the latter case, that the diagonal matrix elements of the angular-momentum operators ($J_{\pm 1}$) vanish. An alternative presentation of the classical description of this section has been given by Franz (50). The quantum-mechanical description of the angular momentum in the radiation field has been given by Heitler (36) and by DeWitt and Jensen (53). Representing the general electromagnetic field as a superposition of multipoles with amplitudes a_σ, where σ is a collective index representing L, M, k, and τ ($\tau = m$ or e), the quantization of the field requires that these amplitudes no longer commute. Instead

$$a_\sigma a_{\sigma'}^* - a_{\sigma'}^* a_\sigma = \delta_{\sigma\sigma'}$$

In a representation in which

$$\tfrac{1}{2}(a_\sigma a_\sigma^* + a_\sigma^* a_\sigma)$$

is diagonal, with the eigenvalues $N_\sigma + \frac{1}{2}$, we find, by evaluation of the energy and angular momentum integrals, (3.29) and (3.30),

$$W = \sum_\sigma (N_\sigma + \tfrac{1}{2})\hbar\omega_\sigma$$

$$G_0 = \sum_\sigma N_\sigma \hbar M$$

where N_σ is the number of quanta in the state σ of the radiation field. For the off-diagonal components of the angular momentum we obtain

$$G_{\pm 1} = \mp \frac{1}{\sqrt{2}} \sum_\sigma \frac{\hbar}{2} \{ \sqrt{(L \mp M)(L \pm M + 1)}\, a_\sigma(M)\, a_\sigma^*(M \pm 1)$$
$$+ \sqrt{(L \pm M)(L \mp M + 1)}\, a_\sigma^*(M)\, a_\sigma(M \mp 1) \}$$

where the M values associated with the amplitudes a_σ are indicated explicitly. For further details the reader may consult the references cited above.

[3] It will be noted that ordinary units are used here for the angular momentum.

IV. THE RETARDED ELECTROMAGNETIC INTERACTION

20. PRELIMINARY REMARKS

In preceding chapters consideration has been given to the multipole fields in free space. Obviously every electromagnetic field must be generated by a (dynamical) charge distribution. Consequently, in any actual situation the sources of the field must be taken into account. In the first part of this chapter we consider the solutions of the Maxwell equations with sources present and obtain a representation of the source distribution in terms of its multipole moments. The remainder of the chapter is concerned with the application to a quantum-mechanical system of two charged particles and the dynamical interaction between them. The results obtained are then directly applicable to a number of problems such as internal conversion of orbital electrons and Auger transitions. The internal conversion problem will be treated in some detail in Chapter V.

21. EXPANSION OF THE DYADIC GREEN'S FUNCTION

In the presence of sources the vector and scalar potentials are given by the retarded potential solutions (1.13) of the inhomogeneous wave equations. Since we shall be concerned only with the magnetic field strength in the following, it is sufficient to consider the vector potential as given by (1.13*a*). Then

$$\mathbf{A}(\mathbf{r}) = \frac{1}{c} \int \mathbf{j}_0(\mathbf{r}') \cdot \mathbf{I}\, G_0(\mathbf{r}, \mathbf{r}')\, d\mathbf{r}' \tag{4.1}$$

where $\mathbf{I}$ is the unit dyadic. In the spherical basis this is

$$\mathbf{I} = \sum_{\mu} (-)^{\mu} \boldsymbol{\xi}_{\mu}\, \boldsymbol{\xi}_{-\mu} \tag{4.2}$$

so that for any vector $\mathbf{j}_0$

$$\mathbf{j}_0 \cdot \mathbf{I} = \mathbf{I} \cdot \mathbf{j}_0 = \mathbf{j}_0$$

The dyadic $G_0\mathbf{I}$, the so-called dyadic Green's function, may now be expanded in terms of the complete set of multipole potentials. For this purpose we use the notation $\mathbf{A}_L^M(\tau)$ for the standing waves and $\mathbf{B}_L^M(\tau)$ for the outgoing waves. That is, $\mathbf{A}_L^M(\tau)$ are the tensors given by (2.63)–(2.65) with $\zeta_L = f_L$, and $\mathbf{B}_L^M(\tau)$ is obtained from these tensors by setting $\zeta_L = g_L$. From (1.22) it follows that

$$G_0\mathbf{I} = 2\pi^2 ik \sum_{LM} U_L^{M*}(\mathbf{r}_<)\, V_L^M(\mathbf{r}_>) \sum_\mu (-)^\mu \boldsymbol{\xi}_\mu\, \boldsymbol{\xi}_{-\mu} \tag{4.3}$$

in terms of the notation of (1.16) and (1.19). The standing-wave multipole potentials are

$$\mathbf{A}_L^M(m) = -\sum_\mu C(1LL; -\mu, \mu+M)\, U_L^{M+\mu}\, \boldsymbol{\xi}_{-\mu} \tag{4.4a}$$

$$\mathbf{A}_L^M(e) = \frac{1}{\sqrt{2L+1}} \{-\sqrt{L} \sum_\mu C(1\; L+1\; L; -\mu, M+\mu)\, U_{L+1}^{M+\mu}\, \boldsymbol{\xi}_{-\mu}$$
$$+ \sqrt{L+1} \sum_\mu C(1\; L-1\; L; -\mu, M+\mu)\, U_{L-1}^{M+\mu}\, \boldsymbol{\xi}_{-\mu}\} \tag{4.4b}$$

$$\mathbf{A}_L^M(l) = \frac{1}{\sqrt{2L+1}} \{\sqrt{L+1} \sum_\mu C(1\; L+1\; L; -\mu, M+\mu)\, U_{L+1}^{M+\mu}\, \boldsymbol{\xi}_{-\mu}$$
$$+ \sqrt{L} \sum_\mu C(1\; L-1\; L; -\mu, M+\mu)\, U_{L-1}^{M+\mu}\, \boldsymbol{\xi}_{-\mu}\} \tag{4.4c}$$

and the outgoing-wave potentials are obtained by replacing U_L^M by V_L^M. From (4.4*b*) and (4.4*c*) it is seen that

$$\sum_{LM} \sum_\tau \mathbf{B}_L^M(\tau; \mathbf{r})\, \mathbf{A}_L^{M*}(\tau; \mathbf{r}') = \sum_{LM} \sum_{\mu\mu'\rho}$$
$$[C(1\; L+\rho\; L; -\mu, M+\mu)\, C(1\; L+\rho\; L; -\mu', M+\mu')\, V_{L+\rho}^{M+\mu}\, U_{L+\rho}^{M+\mu'*}]$$
$$\times (-)^{\mu'} \boldsymbol{\xi}_{-\mu}\, \boldsymbol{\xi}_{\mu'}$$

where $\rho = \pm 1$ and 0. The sum over L and ρ is carried out by keeping $L + \rho = L'$ fixed and first summing over L. Then only the product of the two C-coefficients is involved in the L-sum, which gives $\delta_{\mu\mu'}$ by (2.18). In the sums over μ and M we set $\mu + M = M'$ and the summation indices are μ and M'. Dropping the primes on L' and M' we find, for $r > r'$,

$$G_0\mathbf{I} = 2\pi^2 ik \sum_{LM\tau} \mathbf{B}_L^M(\tau; \mathbf{r})\, \mathbf{A}_L^{M*}(\tau; \mathbf{r}') \tag{4.5}$$

For greater clarity the argument vectors $\mathbf{r}$ and $\mathbf{r}'$, indicating the point in space at which the potentials are to be evaluated, have been inserted.

For $r < r'$ the arguments $\mathbf{r}$ and $\mathbf{r}'$ in (4.5) are interchanged. The sum over L includes the term $L = 0$, but, of course, only the longitudinal field ($\tau = l$) contributes to this term. It is recognized that in the expantion of the dyadic Green's function as given by (4.5) the electric and magnetic multipoles must be in the solenoidal gauge. The expansion is not gauge invariant, although, of course, expansions in other gauges forming a complete set do exist. The expansion (4.5) has been given in the literature by Morse and Feshbach (53).

22. THE MULTIPOLE MOMENTS

As is well known, the current-charge distribution can be characterized by a set of constants which describe the electric and magnetic moments of the distribution. We define these constants $a_L^M(e)$ and $a_L^M(m)$ by the following expansion for the magnetic field strength:[1]

$$\mathbf{H} = \sqrt{\frac{\pi}{2}} \sum_{LM} \{ia_L^M(e)\, g_L\, \mathbf{T}_{LL}^M - \frac{1}{k}\, a_L^M(m) \operatorname{curl} g_L\, \mathbf{T}_{LL}^M\} \tag{4.6}$$

$$= \sqrt{\frac{\pi}{2}} \frac{1}{k} \sum_{LM} \{a_L^M(e)\mathbf{H}_L^M(e) + a_L^M(m)\, \mathbf{H}_L^M(m)\}$$

valid outside the source.

From (4.1), with $\mathfrak{M} = 0$,

$$\mathbf{H} = \frac{2\pi^2 ik}{c} \sum_{LM\tau} \operatorname{curl} \mathbf{B}_L^M(\tau) \int \mathbf{j}_0(\mathbf{r}') \cdot \mathbf{A}_L^{M*}(\tau)\, d\mathbf{r}' \tag{4.7}$$

where $\mathbf{B}_L^M$ is evaluated at the field point $\mathbf{r}$ and $\mathbf{A}_L^{M*}$ at the source point $\mathbf{r}'$. In comparing (4.6) and (4.7) we use

$$\mathbf{B}_L^M(e) = \frac{1}{ik} \operatorname{curl} \mathbf{B}_L^M(m)$$

$$\mathbf{B}_L^M(m) = \frac{i}{k} \operatorname{curl} \mathbf{B}_L^M(e)$$

with

$$\mathbf{B}_L^M(m) = -g_L\, \mathbf{T}_{LL}^M$$

It is also to be noted that in (4.7) only $\tau = e$ and m contribute. The

[1] With the normalization we have used, the free space field strengths $\mathbf{H}_L^M(\tau)$ have the dimensions of a reciprocal length. On the other hand the dimensions of $\mathbf{H}$ and therefore of $a_L^M(\tau)$ are those of a field strength [charge divided by (length)^2].

comparison shows that

$$a_L^M(m) = (2\pi)^{3/2} \frac{ik^2}{c} \int f_L(kr') \, \mathbf{j}_0(\mathbf{r}') \cdot \mathbf{T}_{LL}^{M*} \, d\mathbf{r}' \tag{4.8}$$

and

$$a_L^M(e) = -(2\pi)^{3/2} \frac{k}{c} \int \mathbf{j}_0 \cdot \text{curl } \mathbf{A}_L^{M*}(m) \, d\mathbf{r}'$$

$$= -(2\pi)^{3/2} \frac{k}{c} \int \mathbf{A}_L^{M*}(m) \cdot \text{curl } \mathbf{j}_0 \, d\mathbf{r}'$$

wherein

$$\text{div } \mathbf{C} \times \mathbf{D} = \mathbf{D} \cdot \text{curl } \mathbf{C} - \mathbf{C} \cdot \text{curl } \mathbf{D}$$

is used. Finally, substituting the tensor form for $\mathbf{A}_L^M(m)$ we obtain

$$a_L^M(e) = (2\pi)^{3/2} \frac{k}{c} \int f_L(kr') \, \mathbf{T}_{LL}^{M*} \cdot \text{curl } \mathbf{j}_0 \, d\mathbf{r}' \tag{4.9}$$

The results (4.8) and (4.9) were obtained on the assumption of zero magnetization, $\mathfrak{M} = 0$. The contribution due to a volume distribution of magnetization is easily obtained by replacing $\mathbf{j}_0$ by

$$\mathbf{j}_0 + c \text{ curl } \mathfrak{M}_0$$

and curl $\mathbf{j}_0$ by

$$\text{curl } \mathbf{j}_0 + ck^2 \mathfrak{M}_0$$

In most practical cases the wavelength of the radiation is much larger than the linear dimensions of the sources. For example, for the emission of a 1-Mev γ-ray by a medium-weight nucleus, $kr \lesssim 0.03$. In the case $kR \ll 1$, where R is the nuclear radius, or more generally, the maximum value of r' which contributes to the multipole moment integrals, the results (4.8) and (4.9) can be re-expressed in simpler form. For the electric multipole moment we use

$$\mathbf{T}_{LL}^{M*} \cdot \text{curl } \mathbf{j}_0 = -\frac{(\mathbf{L} Y_L^M)^*}{\sqrt{L(L+1)}} \cdot \text{curl } \mathbf{j}_0$$

so that

$$\int f_L \, \mathbf{T}_{LL}^{M*} \cdot \text{curl } \mathbf{j}_0 \, d\mathbf{r}' = -\frac{1}{\sqrt{L(L+1)}} \int (\mathbf{L} \cdot \text{curl } \mathbf{j}_0) \, Y_L^{M*} f_L \, d\mathbf{r}'$$

by the hermitian property of $\mathbf{L}$. Further

$$\mathbf{L}\cdot\text{curl}\,\mathbf{j}_0 = -i\left\{\left(2 + r\frac{\partial}{\partial r}\right)\text{div}\,\mathbf{j}_0 - \nabla^2(\mathbf{r}\cdot\mathbf{j}_0)\right\}$$

and

$$\text{div}\,\mathbf{j}_0 = i\omega\rho_0$$

by the continuity equation. Using the hermitian property of the Laplace operator the integral in (4.9) takes the form

$$\int f_L\,\mathbf{T}_{LL}^{M*}\cdot\text{curl}\,\mathbf{j}_0\,d\mathbf{r}'$$

$$= \frac{i}{\sqrt{L(L+1)}}\int Y_L^{M*} f_L\left[\left(2 + r'\frac{\partial}{\partial r'}\right)i\omega\rho_0 + k^2\mathbf{r}'\cdot\mathbf{j}_0\right]d\mathbf{r}'$$

$$= -\frac{i}{\sqrt{L(L+1)}}\int Y_L^{M*}\left\{\left(r'\frac{df_L}{dr'} + f_L\right)i\omega\rho_0 - k^2 f_L\,\mathbf{r}'\cdot\mathbf{j}_0\right\}d\mathbf{r}'$$

where the last form is obtained after an integration of the $\partial\rho_0/\partial r'$ term by parts. The condition $kr' \ll 1$, which has not been used up to this point, gives

$$r'\frac{df_L}{dr'} + f_L \approx \sqrt{\frac{2}{\pi}}\frac{L+1}{(2L+1)!!}(kr')^L$$

On the other hand the ratio of the second to the first term is

$$\frac{k^2\mathbf{r}'\cdot\mathbf{j}_0}{\omega\rho_0} \sim (kr')^2$$

since $\text{div}\,\mathbf{j}_0 \sim |\mathbf{j}_0|/r'$. Hence, the second term is negligible compared to the first, and we obtain the result

$$a_L^M(e) = \frac{4\pi}{(2L+1)!!}\sqrt{\frac{L+1}{L}}\,k^{L+2}\int r'^L\,Y_L^{M*}\,\rho_0(\mathbf{r}')\,d\mathbf{r}' \qquad (4.10)$$

A similar reduction may be carried out for the magnetic multipole moment:

$$f_L\,\mathbf{j}_0\cdot\mathbf{T}_{LL}^{M*} = -\frac{f_L}{\sqrt{L(L+1)}}(\mathbf{L}\,Y_L^M)^*\cdot\mathbf{j}_0$$

$$= -\frac{if_L}{\sqrt{L(L+1)}}\nabla Y_L^{M*}\cdot\mathbf{r}\times\mathbf{j}_0$$

Therefore

$$\int f_L\, \mathbf{j}_0 \cdot \mathbf{T}_{LL}^{M*}\, d\mathbf{r}' = -\frac{i}{\sqrt{L(L+1)}} \int \nabla(f_L\, Y_L^{M*}) \cdot \mathbf{r}' \times \mathbf{j}_0\, d\mathbf{r}'$$

$$= \frac{i}{\sqrt{L(L+1)}} \int f_L\, Y_L^{M*} \operatorname{div}(\mathbf{r}' \times \mathbf{j}_0)\, d\mathbf{r}'$$

Consequently, in the long-wavelength limit

$$a_L^M(m) = -\frac{4\pi}{(2L+1)!!} \frac{1}{\sqrt{L(L+1)}} \frac{k^{L+2}}{c} \int r'^L\, Y_L^{M*} \operatorname{div}(\mathbf{r}' \times \mathbf{j}_0)\, d\mathbf{r}' \tag{4.11}$$

It will be recognized that the multipole moments given by (4.10) and (4.11) have the form of the well-known static moments. For example, the integral in (4.10) for $L = 1$ gives the usual electric dipole moment. For $L = 1$ the magnetic multipole moment may be written in more familiar form by observing that $r'\, Y_1^{M*}$ are essentially the components of the vector $\mathbf{r}'$ and

$$\int \mathbf{r}' \operatorname{div} \mathbf{r}' \times \mathbf{j}_0\, d\mathbf{r}' = -\int \mathbf{r}' \times \mathbf{j}_0\, d\mathbf{r}'$$

by Gauss's theorem.

The circumstance that the exact form for $a_L^M(e)$ depends on curl $\mathbf{j}_0$, that is, the transverse (or solenoidal) current density, while the approximate form (4.10) depends on ρ_0 or div $\mathbf{j}_0$ which involves only the longitudinal (or irrotational) current density, is explained by French and Shimamoto (53) as a consequence of the fact that these two constituents of the current density are not independent. Indeed, outside the source, the total current, which is the sum of transverse and longitudinal parts, vanishes identically.

23. THE INTERACTION BETWEEN TWO CHARGES: GENERAL DISCUSSION

The results of the foregoing sections provide a description of the field generated at a point $\mathbf{r}$ due to a given source. If the charge and current density at $\mathbf{r}'$ are given by $\rho_0(\mathbf{r}')$ and $\mathbf{j}_0(\mathbf{r}')$ the classical interaction energy is

$$\mathfrak{U} = \int [\rho_0(\mathbf{r}')\, U(\mathbf{r}') - \frac{1}{c}\, \mathbf{j}_0(\mathbf{r}') \cdot \mathbf{A}(\mathbf{r}')]\, d\mathbf{r}' \tag{4.12}$$

In this section we consider the quantum-mechanical description of the interaction energy. Explicit results can be obtained only when the equations of motion of the interacting systems are fully specified. One of these systems will be taken to be a Dirac electron. However, the results of the present section will be applied in sec. 27 to the internal conversion problem where the interaction between a Dirac electron and a nucleus is the problem of chief concern. For reasons to be discussed below, the equations of motion (hamiltonian equation) for a nucleus coupled to an electromagnetic field depend intimately on the essentially unknown nuclear forces. For this reason, in most of this section, the dynamical description for one system (the nucleus) will be retained in general form. For the internal conversion coefficient of a point nucleus it is unnecessary to specify the nuclear dynamics in detail. Subsequently, as an illustration of the results to be obtained in this section, we consider the interaction of two Dirac electrons, and in this case the hamiltonian equations can be made explicit throughout.

The total system under consideration consists of the radiation field and two particles, labeled 1 and 2 (the term *particle* includes the case of a nucleus or, more exactly, a nucleon to which the radiation field is coupled). Particle 1 will be a Dirac electron. The hamiltonian equation for the system is

$$i\frac{\partial\psi}{\partial t} = [\mathfrak{H}_1(\overline{\mathbf{A}}) + \mathfrak{H}_2(\overline{\mathbf{A}}) + \mathfrak{H}_R]\psi \qquad (4.13)$$

t designates the time, and the units are such that $\hbar = c = 1$. In (4.13), $\mathfrak{H}_R$ is the hamiltonian of the radiation field alone; $\mathfrak{H}_1(\overline{\mathbf{A}})$ and $\mathfrak{H}_2(\overline{\mathbf{A}})$ refer to particles 1 and 2 in the presence of the field, whose vector potential is $\overline{\mathbf{A}}$. Thus $\mathfrak{H}_1$ and $\mathfrak{H}_2$ contain the coupling terms which represent the interaction between particles and field.

For the Dirac electron

$$\mathfrak{H}_1 = -\boldsymbol{\alpha}\cdot(\mathbf{p} - e_1\overline{\mathbf{A}}) - \beta m + e_1\overline{U} \qquad (4.14)$$

In (4.14), e_1 is the electron charge, m the electron mass; the matrices $\boldsymbol{\alpha}$ and β are

$$\boldsymbol{\alpha} = \begin{pmatrix} 0 & \sigma \\ \sigma & 0 \end{pmatrix} \qquad \beta = \begin{pmatrix} 1 & 0 \\ 0 & -1 \end{pmatrix} \qquad (4.14')$$

where each element is a two-by-two matrix and $\boldsymbol{\sigma}$ is defined in (2.4). Obviously (4.14) can be written as

$$\mathfrak{H}_1 = \mathfrak{H}_1(0) + \mathfrak{H}_1(\overline{\mathbf{A}})$$

where

$$\mathfrak{H}_1(0) = -\boldsymbol{\alpha}\cdot\mathbf{p} - \beta m \qquad (4.15)$$

is the free-particle hamiltonian and

$$\mathfrak{H}_1(\overline{\mathbf{A}}) = e_1(\boldsymbol{\alpha}\cdot\overline{\mathbf{A}} + \overline{U}) \tag{4.16}$$

is the coupling term. Corresponding to the decomposition of $\overline{\mathbf{A}}$ and $\overline{U}$ into complex fields, we write

$$\mathfrak{H}_1(\overline{\mathbf{A}}) = \mathfrak{H}_1(\mathbf{A})\, e^{-i\omega t} + \mathfrak{H}_1(\mathbf{A}^*)\, e^{i\omega t} \tag{4.16$'$}$$

and $\mathfrak{H}_1(\mathbf{A})$ is the functional of $\mathbf{A}$ defined by the form (4.16).

It is essential to consider the effect of a gauge transformation; see equation 1.24. If the wave functional ψ describes the Dirac electron so that

$$i\,\frac{\partial\psi}{\partial t} = \mathfrak{H}_1\,\psi \tag{4.17}$$

and we make the transformation

$$\psi = e^{-ie_1\overline{S}}\,\psi' \tag{4.18}$$

where $\overline{S}$ is a (one-by-one) function of the coordinates and t, it follows that

$$i\,\frac{\partial\psi'}{\partial t} = \mathfrak{H}_1'\,\psi' \tag{4.19}$$

where

$$\mathfrak{H}_1' = e^{ie_1\overline{S}}\,\mathfrak{H}_1\,e^{-ie_1\overline{S}} - e_1\,\frac{\partial\overline{S}}{\partial t} \tag{4.20}$$

and where $\mathfrak{H}_1$ is given by (4.14). It will be recognized that the result (4.20) is quite general and describes the effect of the unitary transformation ($\overline{S}$ hermitian) on any hamiltonian equation. In the particular case of (4.14) it follows that

$$\mathfrak{H}_1'(\overline{\mathbf{A}}) = \mathfrak{H}_1(\overline{\mathbf{A}}') \tag{4.21}$$

where $\overline{\mathbf{A}}'$ stands for the gauge-transformed potentials as in sec. 3. Equation 4.21 then states that a gauge transformation on the potentials is equivalent to a canonical (unitary) transformation on the basis ψ. A canonical transformation, of course, does not change any physical results (for example, matrix elements of the coupling operators), and so we arrive at the conclusion that physical results such as transition probabilities are independent of the gauge. The importance of this result lies in the fact that it dictates the manner in which we must construct the hamiltonian $\mathfrak{H}(\overline{\mathbf{A}})$ from the free-particle hamiltonian $\mathfrak{H}(0)$ in the general case. Only if the property expressed by (4.21) is fulfilled do we obtain the result that the gauge can be changed without affecting the physical results. The hamiltonian for which (4.21) is fulfilled is then said to be gauge invariant.

For the Dirac electron the construction of the gauge-invariant hamiltonian is well known, and, in fact, as the preceding shows, the required form is precisely that given in (4.14). This is also valid when a central field term (Coulomb interaction) is added to $\mathfrak{H}_1$. However, if there are interaction terms, such as those representing the nuclear forces in $\mathfrak{H}_2(0)$, which do not commute with $\bar{S}$, the gauge-invariant hamiltonian may be much more complicated and its exact form depends on the nature of these (nuclear) interactions. This circumstance has been discussed in detail by Sachs and Austern (51), and, as these authors explicitly demonstrate, the prescription for construction of the gauge-invariant hamiltonian will be different from (4.14) (or its non-relativistic equivalent) if the nuclear forces contain exchange or velocity-dependent interactions. In these cases the coupling to the radiation field is directly dependent on the nuclear interactions.[2] Inasmuch as the latter are not completely understood it is preferable to treat the interaction of the second particle with the radiation field in a general way.

Accordingly, we write for particle 2,

$$\mathfrak{H}_2(\bar{\mathbf{A}}) = \mathfrak{H}(0) + \mathfrak{H}^{(1)}(\bar{\mathbf{A}}) + \mathfrak{H}^{(2)}(\bar{\mathbf{A}}) + \cdots \tag{4.22}$$

which corresponds to an expansion in the vector potential or coupling constant e_2. Thus $\mathfrak{H}(0)$ is the free-particle hamiltonian, $\mathfrak{H}^{(1)}(\bar{\mathbf{A}})$ is a linear homogeneous functional of $\bar{\mathbf{A}}$, $\mathfrak{H}^{(2)}(\bar{\mathbf{A}})$ is homogeneous and of second degree in $\bar{\mathbf{A}}$, etc. Each term in (4.22) is hermitian. In what follows we are interested only in single quantum emission (or absorption) and terms beyond $\mathfrak{H}^{(1)}$ will be dropped. Again,

$$\mathfrak{H}^{(1)}(\bar{\mathbf{A}}) = \mathfrak{H}^{(1)}(\mathbf{A})\, e^{-i\omega t} + \mathfrak{H}^{(1)}(\mathbf{A}^*)\, e^{i\omega t} \tag{4.22$'$}$$

where $\mathbf{A}$, $\mathbf{A}^*$ are time independent.

24. THE INTERACTION BETWEEN TWO CHARGES: SPECIFIC RESULTS[3]

The interaction between particles 1 and 2 takes place via the coupling of each particle with the radiation field. The situation considered is the following: At $t = 0$, particle 1 is in a state of zero energy, particle 2 in an excited state of energy W. This is the initial state and will be

[2] In Chapter V we shall show that this restriction does not apply to the emission (or absorption) of electric multipole radiation in the long-wavelength limit.

[3] The results to be presented in this section were first given by Tralli and Goertzel (51). The procedure adopted here is somewhat different from the one used by these authors.

labeled by the index i. There are two intermediate states described by the following scheme:

	Particle 1	Particle 2	Quantum Energy
State j	0	0	ω
State j'	E	W	ω

That is, for state j a (virtual) quantum of energy ω has been emitted by particle 2 whose energy after emission is zero. For state j' a quantum of energy ω has been emitted by particle 1 which takes the energy E after emission. The final state (label f) is one in which there are no radiation quanta, particle 1 is in the state with energy E, and particle 2 is in the state with zero energy. This state is reached from j (or j') by the absorption of radiation energy ω by particle 1 (or 2).

The total wave function Ψ is expanded into functionals of states i, j, j', f:

$$\Psi = a_i(t)\,\Psi_i + a_j(t)\,\Psi_j + a_{j'}(t)\,\Psi_{j'} + a_f(t)\,\Psi_f$$

Then the equations of motion for the probability amplitudes $a_i \cdots a_f$ take the form

$$i\dot{a}_i = Wa_i + \int d\omega\,\mathfrak{H}_{0\omega}\,a_j(\omega) + \int d\omega\,\mathfrak{H}'_{0\omega}\,a_{j'}(\omega) \tag{4.23a}$$

$$i\dot{a}_j = \omega a_j + \mathfrak{H}_{\omega 0}\,a_i + \int dE\,\mathfrak{H}_{\omega E}\,a_f(E) \tag{4.23b}$$

$$i\dot{a}_{j'} = (\omega + W + E)a_{j'} + \mathfrak{H}'_{\omega 0}\,a_i + \int dE\,\mathfrak{H}'_{\omega E}\,a_f(E) \tag{4.23c}$$

$$i\dot{a}_f = Ea_f + \int d\omega\,\mathfrak{H}_{E\omega}\,a_j(\omega) + \int d\omega\,\mathfrak{H}'_{E\omega}\,a_{j'}(\omega) \tag{4.23d}$$

Here $\int d\omega$ implies an integration over all intermediate photon energies and a sum over τ, L, M, that is, over the complete set of multipole fields in terms of which the general radiation field is expanded. The integration designated by $\int dE$ sums over the energies of the Dirac electron and also implies a spin summation. The matrix elements in (4.23) are defined by

$$\mathfrak{H}_{E\omega} = \sqrt{2\pi\omega}\int d\mathbf{r}_1\,\psi_f^*\,\mathfrak{H}_1(\mathbf{A}_L^M(\tau))\,\psi_i \tag{4.24a}$$

$$\mathfrak{H}'_{E\omega} = \sqrt{2\pi\omega}\int d\mathbf{r}_2\,\Phi_f^*\,\mathfrak{H}^{(1)}(\mathbf{A}_L^M(\tau))\,\Phi_i \tag{4.24b}$$

$$\mathfrak{H}_{\omega 0} = \sqrt{2\pi\omega}\int d\mathbf{r}_2\, \Phi_f^*\, \mathfrak{H}^{(1)}(\mathbf{A}_L^{M*}(\tau))\, \Phi_i \tag{4.24c}$$

$$\mathfrak{H}'_{\omega 0} = \sqrt{2\pi\omega}\int d\mathbf{r}_1\, \psi_f^*\, \mathfrak{H}_1(\mathbf{A}_L^{M*}(\tau))\, \psi_i \tag{4.24d}$$

Here ψ_i and ψ_f refer to particle 1, and Φ_i and Φ_f refer to particle 2. Equations 4.23 are to be solved subject to the initial conditions

$$a_i = 1, \quad a_j = a_{j'} = a_f = 0, \qquad \text{at } t = 0.$$

The solution will be effected by the standard methods of perturbation theory [for example, Schiff (49)], and the lowest non-vanishing order will be considered. This implies that in (4.23*a*) the second and third terms on the right-hand side are neglected and in (4.23*b*) as well as (4.23*c*) the third terms are dropped. Then

$$a_i = e^{-iWt} \tag{4.25a}$$

$$a_j = \frac{\mathfrak{H}_{\omega 0}}{\omega - W}\,(e^{-i\omega t} - e^{-iWt}) \tag{4.25b}$$

$$a_{j'} = \frac{\mathfrak{H}'_{\omega 0}}{\omega + E}\, e^{-iWt}(e^{-i(\omega+E)t} - 1) \tag{4.25c}$$

$$\begin{aligned} a_f = &\int d\omega\, \frac{\mathfrak{H}_{E\omega}\,\mathfrak{H}_{\omega 0}}{W - \omega}\left[\frac{e^{i(E-W)t} - 1}{E - W} - \frac{e^{i(E-\omega)t} - 1}{E - \omega}\right] \\ &+ \int d\omega\, \frac{\mathfrak{H}'_{E\omega}\,\mathfrak{H}'_{\omega 0}}{\omega + E}\left[\frac{e^{i(E-W)t} - 1}{E - W} + \frac{e^{-i(W+\omega)t} - 1}{W + \omega}\right] \end{aligned} \tag{4.25d}$$

The second and fourth terms do not conserve energy between the initial and final state, and only the first and third terms, which do conserve energy and which do lead to a transition probability increasing linearly with the time, are retained. In the usual fashion we obtain for the number of transitions to the final state

$$\int dE\,|a_f|^2 = 2\pi t\,|\mathfrak{H}_{fi}|^2$$

and for the number of transitions per unit time

$$\nu = 2\pi\,|\mathfrak{H}_{fi}|^2 \tag{4.26}$$

where

$$\mathfrak{H}_{fi} = \int d\omega\left[\frac{\mathfrak{H}_{E\omega}\,\mathfrak{H}_{\omega 0}}{W - \omega + i\eta} + \frac{\mathfrak{H}'_{E\omega}\,\mathfrak{H}'_{\omega 0}}{\omega + E - i\eta}\right] \tag{4.27}$$

evaluated at $W = E$. In (4.27) the path of integration is along the real axis from $\omega = 0$ to $\omega = \infty$. The displacement of the poles into the upper half-plane is effected by the addition of the term $i\eta$ $(\eta \geq 0)$ in the energy denominators.

The matrix element $\mathfrak{H}_{fi}$ can be expressed in the form

$$\mathfrak{H}_{fi} = \int d\omega \, \frac{\mathfrak{H}_{E\omega} \, \mathfrak{H}_{\omega 0}}{W - \omega + i\eta} \tag{4.27'}$$

with the path extending over the entire real ω-axis. In general, from (4.24),

$$\mathfrak{H}_{fi} = 2\pi \int \frac{\omega \, d\omega}{W - \omega + i\eta} \sum_{LM\tau} \int d\mathbf{r}_1 \, \psi_f^* \, \mathfrak{H}_1(\mathbf{A}_L^M(\tau)) \, \psi_i \times \int d\mathbf{r}_2 \, \Phi_f^* \, \mathfrak{H}^{(1)}(\mathbf{A}_L^{M*}(\tau)) \, \Phi_i \tag{4.28}$$

where the multipole summation is now explicitly indicated.

The ω-integration is now carried out by closing the path with a large semicircular loop in the lower or upper half-plane. Since both $\mathfrak{H}_1$ and $\mathfrak{H}^{(1)}$ are linear in the potentials and since for the standing waves appearing in (4.28) the radial function involves f_L, where

$$f_L = \tfrac{1}{2}(g_L + g_L^*)$$

the asymptotic behavior of each operator will consist of two parts: viz., one containing the factor $e^{i\omega r}$ (see equation 3.23) from g_L, and one containing $e^{-i\omega r}$ from g_L^*. For $r_1 \lessgtr r_2$ the product $\mathfrak{H}_1 \, \mathfrak{H}^{(1)}$ contains four terms proportional to $e^{i\omega(r_1+r_2)}$, $e^{i\omega(r_1-r_2)}$, $e^{-i\omega(r_1-r_2)}$, $e^{-i\omega(r_1+r_2)}$, respectively. For $r_1 > r_2$ the path can be closed in the upper half-plane for the first two. For the second two, with exponents which have a negative coefficient of $i\omega$, the path must be closed in the lower half-plane and hence these terms contribute nothing. Therefore, only the outgoing part $(e^{i\omega r_1})$ of the standing wave in $\mathbf{r}_1$ space contributes to the integral. Thus, in evaluating the residue in (4.28) we replace $f_L(r_1)$ by $\frac{1}{2}g_L(r_1)$. This means that $\mathbf{A}_L^M(\tau)$ in $\mathbf{r}_1$ space is replaced by $\frac{1}{2}\mathbf{B}_L^M(\tau)$. Thus, for $r_1 > r_2$,

$$\mathfrak{H}_{fi} = -2\pi^2 ik \sum_{LM\tau} \int d\mathbf{r}_1 \, \psi_f^* \, \mathfrak{H}_1(\mathbf{B}_L^M(\tau)) \, \psi_i \int d\mathbf{r}_2 \, \Phi_f^* \, \mathfrak{H}^{(1)}(\mathbf{A}_L^{M*}(\tau)) \, \Phi_i \tag{4.29}$$

Similarly, for $r_2 > r_1$,

$$\mathfrak{H}_{fi} = -2\pi^2 ik \sum_{LM\tau} \int d\mathbf{r}_1 \, \psi_f^* \, \mathfrak{H}_1(\mathbf{A}_L^M(\tau)) \, \psi_i \int d\mathbf{r}_2 \, \Phi_f^* \, \mathfrak{H}^{(1)}(\mathbf{B}_L^{M*}(\tau)) \, \Phi_i \tag{4.29'}$$

where we have introduced $W = E = k$, on the basis of energy conservation, and in the matrix elements of (4.29′) we must set $\omega = k$. This result will form the basis of the treatment of the internal conversion problem; see Chapter V.

For the interaction of the particles we consider two Dirac electrons.[4] Then both $\mathfrak{H}_1$ and $\mathfrak{H}^{(1)}$ in (4.27′) have the form (4.16) and

$$\mathfrak{H}_{fi} = 2\pi e_1 e_2 \int \frac{\omega\, d\omega}{W - \omega + i\eta} \sum_{LM\tau} \int d\mathbf{r}_1\, \psi_f^* (\boldsymbol{\alpha}_1 \cdot \mathbf{A}_L^M(\tau) + U_L^M(\tau))\, \psi_i$$

$$\times \int d\mathbf{r}_2\, \Phi_f^* \,(\boldsymbol{\alpha}_2 \cdot \mathbf{A}_L^{M*}(\tau) + U_L^{M*}(\tau))\, \Phi_i \quad (4.30)$$

Since both matrix elements are gauge invariant, no loss of generality is incurred by using the solenoidal gauge. Then $U(\tau) = 0$ except for $\tau = l$, and in this case

$$\mathbf{A}_L^M(\tau) = \nabla S$$

$$U_L^M(\tau) = i\omega S$$

where S is defined by (2.66). For the longitudinal terms we have

$$\boldsymbol{\alpha}_1 \cdot \mathbf{A}_L^M(l, \mathbf{r}_1) = \boldsymbol{\alpha}_1 \cdot \nabla S = i(S\mathfrak{H}_1(0) - \mathfrak{H}_1(0)S)$$

and a similar result applies for $\boldsymbol{\alpha}_2 \cdot \mathbf{A}_L^{M*}(l, \mathbf{r}_2)$. Using the hermitian property of $\mathfrak{H}_i(0)$ and

$$\mathfrak{H}_1(0)\, \psi_i = 0$$

$$\mathfrak{H}_1(0)\, \psi_f = E\, \psi_f$$

$$\mathfrak{H}_2(0)\, \Phi_i = W\, \Phi_i$$

$$\mathfrak{H}_2(0)\, \Phi_f = 0$$

the matrix element in (4.30) reduces to

$$\mathfrak{H}_{fi} = 2\pi e_1 e_2 \int \frac{\omega\, d\omega}{W - \omega + i\eta} \sum_{LM\tau} \iint d\mathbf{r}_1\, d\mathbf{r}_2\, \psi_f^*\, \Phi_f^*$$

$$\times \left\{ \boldsymbol{\alpha}_1 \cdot \mathbf{A}_L^M(\tau)\, \boldsymbol{\alpha}_2 \cdot \mathbf{A}_L^{M*}(\tau) + \left(1 - \frac{W + E}{\omega}\right) U_L^M(\tau)\, U_L^{M*}(\tau) \right\}$$

where the starred potentials are in the space $\mathbf{r}_2$ and the unstarred potentials are in the space $\mathbf{r}_1$. Carrying out the ω-integration as before the

[4] In this case it is necessary to antisymmetrize either the initial-state wave function $\psi_i\, \Phi_i$ or the final wave function $\psi_f\, \Phi_f$ of the electron pair. This need not be done *explicitly* for the considerations of this section.

result obtained for $r_1 > r_2$ is

$$\mathfrak{H}_{fi} = -2\pi^2 i e_1 e_2 k \sum_{LM\tau} \iint d\mathbf{r}_1\, d\mathbf{r}_2\, \psi_f^*\, \Phi_f^*$$

$$\times \{\boldsymbol{\alpha}_1 \cdot \mathbf{B}_L^M(\tau, \mathbf{r}_1)\, \boldsymbol{\alpha}_2 \cdot \mathbf{A}_L^{M*}(\tau, \mathbf{r}_2) - U_L^M(\tau, \mathbf{r}_1)\, U_L^{M*}(\tau, r_2)\} \quad (4.31)$$

From the expansion of the dyadic and scalar Green's functions, (4.5) and (1.22), this becomes

$$\mathfrak{H}_{fi} = e_1 e_2 \iint d\mathbf{r}_1\, d\mathbf{r}_2\, \psi_f^*\, \Phi_f^*\, G_0(1 - \boldsymbol{\alpha}_1 \cdot \boldsymbol{\alpha}_2)\psi_i\, \Phi_i \quad (4.32)$$

This means that the interaction operator between the two electrons, the matrix elements of which determine the transition probability, is

$$\mathcal{W} = e_1 e_2 (1 - \boldsymbol{\alpha}_1 \cdot \boldsymbol{\alpha}_2) \frac{e^{ik|\mathbf{r}_1 - \mathbf{r}_2|}}{|\mathbf{r}_1 - \mathbf{r}_2|} \quad (4.33)$$

This corresponds exactly to the retarded interaction between two relativistically moving particles. That is, $\psi_f^*\, \Phi_f^*(1 - \boldsymbol{\alpha}_1 \cdot \boldsymbol{\alpha}_2)\psi_i\, \Phi_i$ is the contraction between the two current four-vectors, and the Green's function G_0 represents the retardation. The operator $\mathcal{W}$, or the matrix element (4.32), is used in the relativistic theory of the Auger effect [Massey and Burhop (36)]. The result (4.33) was first obtained by Hulme (36).

V. INTERNAL CONVERSION

25. DEFINITION OF THE INTERNAL CONVERSION COEFFICIENT

A nucleus in an excited state in making a transition to a state of lower energy may emit a gamma ray or, alternatively, the energy released may be utilized to eject an atomic electron from one of the bound states into the continuous energy spectrum. The mechanism of the latter process has been described in sec. 23. The two processes are competing in the sense that one or the other takes place when a given nucleus makes a transition.[1] The internal conversion coefficient is a measure of the relative probability of the two processes and is defined as the ratio of the total number of ejected (conversion) electrons per unit time to the total rate of emission of gamma rays. This means that N_e, the number of electrons ejected per second, is given by (4.26) summed over all directions of emission and all substates of the initial (bound) state and final (continuum) state. This summation is indicated by the symbol $\mathfrak{S}$. Thus

$$N_e = 2\pi\mathfrak{S}|\mathfrak{H}_{fi}|^2 \tag{5.1}$$

The integration over all directions of emission is automatically taken into account by the angular-momentum representation of the electron wave functions used below; see equation 5.8. Clearly, the wave number k which appears in the explicit form of $\mathfrak{H}_{fi}$, (4.29), is, in our units, just the energy released in the nuclear transition.

The total number of quanta emitted per second, N_q, is given by

$$N_q = \frac{d}{dt}\int d\omega\,|a_j|^2$$

and from (4.25*b*) this is

$$\begin{aligned} N_q &= 4|\mathfrak{H}_{k0}|^2 \frac{d}{dt}\int_{-\infty}^{\infty} \frac{\sin^2 \frac{1}{2}(\omega - W)t}{(\omega - W)^2}\, d(\omega - W) \\ &= 2\pi|\mathfrak{H}_{k0}|^2 \end{aligned} \tag{5.2}$$

[1] This is aside from the alternative possibility that the energy (if >1.02 Mev) appears as an electron-positron pair. The ratio of pairs to gamma rays is about 10^{-4} to 10^{-3}.

Let us consider a nucleus of negligible dimension so that (4.29) would apply. The matrix element appears then as a sum (over L, M) of products of two matrix elements, one in electron space and one in nuclear space. We abbreviate the notation by writing this in the form

$$\mathfrak{H}_{fi} = -2\pi^2 ik \sum_{LM\tau} (f|\mathfrak{H}_1(\mathbf{B}_L^M(\tau))|i)(f|\mathfrak{H}^{(1)}(\mathbf{A}_L^{M*}(\tau))|i) \qquad (5.3)$$

From the transformation properties of $\mathbf{A}_L^M$ it is clear from the Eckart theorem that if J_i and J_f are the angular momenta of the nuclear states then the triangular condition $\Delta(J_iJ_fL)$ applies in the Lth term of the sum. This, of course, is an expression of the angular-momentum conservation. The parity conservation is expressed by

$$\pi_i \pi_f = \pi_r$$

where π_r is the parity of $\mathfrak{H}^{(1)}(\mathbf{A}_L^{M*}(\tau))$. If the nuclear forces are of the ordinary type $\mathfrak{H}^{(1)} \sim \mathbf{A}_L^{M*}\cdot\nabla$ (see equation 6.24 below) and the parity π_r is $(-)^L$ for electric multipoles and $(-)^{L+1}$ for magnetic multipoles. This conclusion will not be changed whatever the nuclear forces may be. The consequence of the selection rules is that only a finite number of terms appear in (5.3). From the discussion of multipole moments in sec. 22 it follows that the matrix element $(f|\mathfrak{H}^{(1)}(\mathbf{A}_L^{M*}(\tau))|i)$ changes by a factor kR when L increases by 1 unit. Here R is the nuclear radius. This result is borne out in Chapter VI, where explicit results for the transition rates are given. Hence, since $kR \ll 1$ in practical cases, the minimum possible value of L will generally be the most important. We designate the electric and magnetic 2^L pole radiations (or transitions) by EL and ML, respectively. For a spin change $|\Delta J| = |J_i - J_f|$, we have, in many cases, $L = |\Delta J|$, and for $|\Delta J|$ odd (even) the radiation would be electric, EL (magnetic, ML) for $\pi_i = -\pi_f$. For $\pi_i = \pi_f$ and $L = |\Delta J|$ electric radiation occurs for $|\Delta J|$ even and magnetic for $|\Delta J|$ odd. In Chapter VI it will be pointed out that ML and $E(L+1)$ radiation may be of comparable intensity.

For the internal conversion coefficients there can be no interference between different L-, different M-, and different τ-values. This can be shown quite easily from a simple extension of the formalism appearing below in sec. 27. The lack of M-interference is obvious from conservation of the z-component of total angular momentum, equation 5.20, and the fact that the various substates of ψ_i and ψ_f are incoherent in the envisaged process.

Finally, it is readily seen that for a point nucleus the longitudinal field makes no contribution to (5.3). This is simply the statement of gauge invariance. Actually, the principle of gauge invariance must be applied rather carefully here, and attention is given to this question in sec. 26.

From these remarks we may write for the conversion coefficient for a particular field (L and τ)

$$\alpha(\tau, L) = N_e/N_q = 2\pi^3 k \mathfrak{S} |(f|\mathfrak{H}_1(\mathbf{B}_L^M(\tau))|i)|^2 \tag{5.4}$$

By virtue of the realistic assumption of a point nucleus the matrix element in nuclear space has canceled out and the internal conversion coefficient is independent of any unknown nuclear properties.[2] In particular it is independent of the unknown form of the operator $\mathfrak{H}^{(1)}$. The only role which the nucleus plays is to act as a source of a "virtual" electromagnetic field with specified energy, angular momentum, and parity. The fact that the latter two properties condition the conversion coefficient constitutes the reason for the importance of this quantity in nuclear physics. In fact, the conversion coefficient is, in general, a rather sensitive function of k, L, and τ ($= e$, or m).

26. THE GAUGE PROBLEM[3]

In the case of electric multipole conversion the result (5.4) is valid only in the conventional gauge. That is, we must use

$$\mathfrak{H}_1(\mathbf{B}_L^M(e)) = e_1(\boldsymbol{\alpha}\cdot\mathbf{B}_L^M + V_L^M) \tag{5.5}$$

where

$$\mathbf{B}_L^M = \sqrt{(2L+1)/(L+1)}\, g_{L-1}\, \mathbf{T}_{LL-1}^M \tag{5.5a}$$

$$V_L^M = i\sqrt{L/(L+1)}\, g_L\, Y_L^M \tag{5.5b}$$

In any other gauge the matrix elements for $\alpha(EL)$ may actually diverge if the wave functions ψ_i and ψ_f are Dirac wave functions for an electron in a Coulomb field. Since the difficulty arises from the singular behavior of these wave functions at the origin, see below, it might be thought that the use of Dirac wave functions for an electron moving in a potential which is less singular at the origin [Rose (51)] would remove the trouble. However, as a simple calculation, similar to that

[2] If the multipole radiation is not pure but is a mixture of, say, ML and $E(L+1)$ the conversion coefficient is seen to be a weighted average of $\alpha(ML)$ and $\alpha(E, L+1)$ where the weights are the relative intensities of the two multipoles. A measurement of the conversion coefficient is often useful as a means of determining this intensity ratio. An estimate of this intensity ratio is obtained in Chapter VI, see equation 6.31′, based on a calculation using the j-j coupling model for the nucleons.

[3] This problem was first discussed by Dancoff and Morrison (39); see also Tralli and Goertzel (51), and Coish (51).

given below, will demonstrate, while the matrix elements are now finite, they are not gauge invariant.

At first sight the fact that the matrix element in (5.4) is not gauge invariant seems to contradict the gauge principle. Actually, this is not so. That the principle of gauge invariance is valid here will be shown in the following. However, first it will be demonstrated that the matrix element in question does have the properties ascribed to it. That the matrix elements for the conventional gauge do converge and are the correct ones to use will be apparent when the calculation of the internal conversion coefficients is considered in greater detail in sec. 27. Therefore it is sufficient to examine the extra terms which arise when a gauge transformation from the solenoidal to the conventional gauge (or any other gauge) is made. These terms are proportional to

$$\Gamma \equiv \int \psi_f^* (\boldsymbol{\alpha} \cdot \nabla S + ikS) \psi_i \, d\mathbf{r} \tag{5.6}$$

where, for the transformation from solenoidal to conventional gauge in the outgoing wave fields, see sec. 12,

$$S = (1/k)\sqrt{L/(L+1)}\, g_L \, Y_L^M \tag{5.7}$$

Again using

$$\boldsymbol{\alpha} \cdot \nabla S = i(S\, \mathfrak{H}(0) - \mathfrak{H}(0)\, S)$$

the matrix element Γ becomes

$$\Gamma = i \int \psi_f^* \{[S, \mathfrak{H}(0)] + kS\} \psi_i \, d\mathbf{r}$$

where the square bracket is the commutator. Denoting the initial and final state electron energies by E_i and E_f respectively, so that $\mathfrak{H}(0)\, \psi_i = E_i \psi_i$ and $\mathfrak{H}(0)\, \psi_f = E_f \psi_f$, and noting that $k = E_f - E_i$, we obtain

$$i\Gamma = \int \psi_f^* \, \mathfrak{H}(0)\, S\, \psi_i \, d\mathbf{r} - \int (\mathfrak{H}(0)\, \psi_f)^* \, S\, \psi_i \, d\mathbf{r}$$

If $\mathfrak{H}(0)$ were hermitian with respect to the functions ψ_f and $S\psi_i$, Γ would vanish. The only term in $\mathfrak{H}(0)$ which needs to be examined is $-\boldsymbol{\alpha} \cdot \mathbf{p}$ and this gives

$$\Gamma = \int \operatorname{div} (\psi_f^* \, \boldsymbol{\alpha}\, S\, \psi_i)\, d\mathbf{r}$$

$$= \Sigma r^2 \int \psi_f^* \, \alpha_r \, S\, \psi_i \, d\Omega$$

where the sum is over the surfaces bounding the region of integration: a sphere at infinity and a small sphere surrounding the origin. The angular integral is exactly the same as that which occurs in the matrix elements of the electric multipole conversion, as may be seen by application of the methods of sec. 27. This is to be expected since otherwise the selection rules would be gauge-dependent. Consequently, we need only examine the radial dependence of Γ on the aforementioned spheres. Clearly, no contribution arises from the infinite sphere. The bound-state wave functions vanish exponentially as r approaches infinity. For the sphere around the origin we use the results that $\psi_f \sim r^{\gamma_f - 1}$ and $\psi_i \sim r^{\gamma_i - 1}$ in a Coulomb field; here

$$\gamma = \sqrt{(j + \tfrac{1}{2})^2 - \alpha^2 Z^2}$$

and (the fine structure constant) $\alpha = e_1^2/\hbar c = e_1^2$ (in these units) $\cong 1/137$. As a consequence $\Gamma \sim r^n$, where

$$n = 2 + (\gamma_f - 1) + (\gamma_i - 1) - L - 1 = \gamma_f + \gamma_i - L - 1$$

and we have used the fact that $g_L \sim r^{-L-1}$ for small r. We set

$$\gamma = j + \tfrac{1}{2} - \delta$$

and it is evident that $0 < \delta \leq 1 - \sqrt{1 - \alpha^2 Z^2}$. From the selection rules, sec. 27, we have $\Delta(j_i j_f L)$, which is the expression of the angular momentum conservation. Hence, there will be one final state with $L = j_f + j_i$. For this case

$$n = -\delta_i - \delta_f < 0$$

Therefore, when the limit $r \to 0$ is taken, Γ diverges in this case. If the Coulomb field is modified to take into account the finite size of the nucleus, the two Dirac radial functions, see (5.8) below, have the indicial behavior

$$f \sim r^{n'} \qquad g \sim r^{n''}$$

where $n' = j - \frac{1}{2}$ or $j + \frac{1}{2}$, where j is the angular momentum of the conversion electron, and $n'' = 2j - n'$. In this case the gauge terms make a finite non-vanishing contribution for the transition cited.

The difficulty, it will be noted, arises from the singular gauge function (5.7), and for the more general gauge function (2.67) with $\zeta_L = g_L$ the situation is no different. This also shows explicitly that for gauge transformations in which the gauge function is a standing wave ($\zeta_L = f_L$), which is regular at the origin, the additional terms of the form (5.6) actually vanish, as expected.

The last statement provides the clue for the solution of the difficulty. First of all, it is to be emphasized that a gauge transformation on the outgoing-wave fields is not expected to be valid. From the discussion of sec. 23 a gauge transformation is valid when applied to the fields which actually occur in a hamiltonian. The outgoing-wave fields never occur in a hamiltonian.[4] In fact, as the results of sec. 24 very clearly indicate, only the standing-wave fields occur in (4.13). As a consequence, before the integration over intermediate state photon frequencies the matrix elements, see equation 4.28, contain only standing-wave fields. At this point any gauge transformation can be made, and after the ω-integration of sec. 24 is carried out the resulting matrix element is (4.29) in whatever gauge was introduced.[5]

This being so, one may well ask why the solenoidal gauge is unsuitable. The answer lies in the simplification made in passing from (4.29) to the form of the matrix element given in (5.3). A tacit assumption is made here, and to see clearly the nature of this assumption one may consider, for the moment, the conversion from a finite size nucleus. Then, the matrix element (4.29) is a sum of three parts: (i) a term in which the electron is outside the nucleus, $r_1 \geq R$ and, of course, $r_2 \leq R$; (ii) a term in which the electron is inside the nucleus but $R \geq r_1 \geq r_2 \geq 0$; (iii) a term in which the electron is again inside the nucleus but $R \geq r_2 \geq r_1 \geq 0$. In obtaining the result (5.3) for $R \to 0$ the terms (ii) and (iii) were dropped. This is permissible only in the less-singular conventional gauge. If any other gauge is used the terms (ii) and (iii) have a non-vanishing limiting form which must be added to (i). In this way one may see the mechanism by which gauge invariance is fulfilled. In the conventional gauge one may not only drop the terms (ii) and (iii) but also extend the range of integration to $0 \leq r_1 \leq \infty$ with negligible error. It is somewhat misleading to refer to the conventional gauge as the "correct gauge," as is sometimes done. Any gauge is correct, but the conventional gauge permits the matrix elements to appear in the simplest possible form.

[4] Presumably part of the confusion in the literature with regard to the gauge problem arises from the fact that (5.4) has the superficial appearance of a first-order process in which the operator $\mathfrak{H}_1(\mathbf{B}_L^M)$ appears as the interaction with the radiation field so that N_e would be $2\pi\mathfrak{S}|(f|\mathfrak{H}_1(\mathbf{B}_L^M)|i)|^2$ and from (3.27), $N_q = 1/\pi^2 k$. Of course, the internal conversion process is actually second order, involving the emission and reabsorption of a virtual quantum of the radiation field.

[5] The solenoidal gauge was used in sec. 24 only for the purpose of obtaining the interaction operator $\mathcal{W}$ of (4.33) in terms of the dyadic Green's function.

27. THE INTERNAL CONVERSION COEFFICIENTS

In this section we treat the problem of reducing the internal conversion coefficients to radial integrals. The latter must then be computed numerically.

As a necessary preliminary the following recapitulation of the Dirac wave functions is given. In a central field the stationary-wave equation

$$(\mathfrak{H}(0) + v)\psi = E\,\psi$$

where v is a central field potential, is separated in polar coordinates by writing

$$\psi = \begin{pmatrix} -if_\kappa \chi^\mu_{-\kappa} \\ g_\kappa \chi^\mu_\kappa \end{pmatrix} \tag{5.8}$$

In (5.8) the symbols are defined as follows: κ is the quantum number (a non-vanishing integer) defining both the parity π_e of the Dirac electron and its angular momentum j according to

$$j = |\kappa| - \tfrac{1}{2} \tag{5.9a}$$

$$\pi_e = (-)^{l_\kappa + 1} \tag{5.9b}$$

and

$$\begin{aligned} l_\kappa &= \kappa \qquad \text{for} \quad \kappa > 0 \\ &= -\kappa - 1 \qquad \text{for} \quad \kappa < 0 \end{aligned} \tag{5.9c}$$

Thus, $j = l_\kappa - \kappa/2|\kappa|$ and $\kappa = -1, -2, -3$ for $s_{1/2}$, $p_{3/2}$, $d_{5/2}$ states while $\kappa = 1, 2, 3$ for $p_{1/2}$, $d_{3/2}$, $f_{5/2}$ states; cf. Bethe (33). The parity π_e is the eigenvalue of the relativistic parity operator $\pi = \beta \times$ space inversion.

The spinors χ^μ_κ, where μ is the eigenvalue of j_z, are defined by

$$\chi^\mu_\kappa = \sum_\tau C(l_\kappa \tfrac{1}{2} j;\, \mu - \tau, \tau)\, \chi^\tau_{1/2}\, Y^{\mu-\tau}_{l_\kappa} \qquad \tau = \pm\tfrac{1}{2} \tag{5.10}$$

where, cf. sec. 6,

$$\chi^{1/2}_{1/2} = \begin{pmatrix} 1 \\ 0 \end{pmatrix} \qquad \chi^{-1/2}_{1/2} = \begin{pmatrix} 0 \\ 1 \end{pmatrix}$$

From the definition χ^μ_κ is an eigenfunction of $\mathbf{j}^2$ and j_z with eigenvalues $j(j+1)$ and μ respectively.[6] Obviously, $\chi^\mu_{-\kappa}$ has the same eigenvalues and is degenerate with χ^μ_κ with respect to $\mathbf{j}^2$ and j_z. These two spinors

[6] Here, and in the following, an operator applied to χ^μ_κ is represented by a two-by-two matrix. Thus, $\mathbf{j} = \mathbf{L} + \tfrac{1}{2}\boldsymbol{\sigma}$. When the same symbol is used as an operator acting on the four-component ψ what is meant is a direct product of the two-by-two matrix and the two-by-two unit matrix; cf. (4.14′).

are distinguished by the fact that

$$(\boldsymbol{\sigma}\cdot\mathbf{L} + 1)\chi_\kappa^\mu = -\kappa\chi_\kappa^\mu \tag{5.11}$$

and are related by

$$\sigma_r\,\chi_\kappa^\mu = -\chi_{-\kappa}^\mu \tag{5.12}$$

Relations (5.11) and (5.12) may be verified directly or derived by a calculation employing the Racah algebra as outlined in sec. 11. Equation 5.11 is equivalent to the well-known fact that χ_κ^μ, multiplied by an appropriate radial function, is a Pauli spinor which diagonalizes the spin-orbit coupling, $\sim\boldsymbol{\sigma}\cdot\mathbf{L}$.

From (5.8) and (5.11) it follows that

$$\beta(\boldsymbol{\sigma}\cdot\mathbf{L} + 1)\psi = \kappa\psi \tag{5.13}$$

Using the fact that

$$(\chi_\kappa^\mu, \chi_{\kappa'}^{\mu'}) = \delta_{\kappa\kappa'}\,\delta_{\mu\mu'} \tag{5.14}$$

where the scalar product in (5.14) means spinor sum and integration over the angular coordinates, and the identity

$$\boldsymbol{\alpha}\cdot\nabla = \rho_1\,\sigma_r\left(\frac{\partial}{\partial r} + \frac{1}{r}\right) - \frac{1}{r}\,\rho_1\sigma_r(\boldsymbol{\sigma}\cdot\mathbf{L} + 1) \tag{5.15}$$

where

$$\rho_1 = \begin{pmatrix} 0 & 1 \\ 1 & 0 \end{pmatrix}$$

and direct products are implied in (5.15), we find from (5.11) and (5.12) that the radial functions fulfill the differential equations

$$\frac{df_\kappa}{dr} = \frac{\kappa - 1}{r} f_\kappa - (E - v - 1)g_\kappa$$

$$\frac{dg_\kappa}{dr} = (E - v + 1)f_\kappa - \frac{\kappa + 1}{r} g_\kappa$$

For a Coulomb field $v = -\alpha Z/r$, and the radial functions for this case have been given by Rose (37).

We now consider the matrix element of (5.4) and treat the magnetic multipole case first. To avoid a multiplicity of indices the final state will be designated by κ, μ and the initial state by κ', μ'. Also $l \equiv l_\kappa$, $l' \equiv l_{\kappa'}$, and $\bar{l} \equiv l_{-\kappa}$, $\bar{l}' \equiv l_{-\kappa'}$. Then

$$K_m \equiv (f|\,\mathfrak{H}_1(\mathbf{B}_L^M(m))\,|i) = \frac{e_1}{\sqrt{L(L + 1)}}\sqrt{\frac{2}{\pi}}\,(f|\,h_L\boldsymbol{\alpha}\cdot\mathbf{L}Y_L^M\,|i) \tag{5.16}$$

where

$$h_L = \sqrt{\frac{\pi}{2kr}}\, H^{(1)}_{L+\frac{1}{2}}(kr)$$

is the usual spherical hankel function of the first kind. Using (5.8) this becomes

$$K_m = \frac{ie_1}{\sqrt{L(L+1)}}\sqrt{\frac{2}{\pi}}\,\{R_1(-\kappa\mu|\boldsymbol{\sigma}\cdot\mathbf{L}Y_L^M|\kappa'\mu') - R_2(\kappa\mu|\boldsymbol{\sigma}\cdot\mathbf{L}Y_L^M|-\kappa'\mu')\} \quad (5.17)$$

Here R_1 and R_2 are radial integrals defined by

$$R_1 = \int_0^\infty f_\kappa\, h_L\, g_{\kappa'}\, r^2\, dr$$

$$R_2 = \int_0^\infty g_\kappa\, h_L\, f_{\kappa'}\, r^2\, dr$$

The matrix elements in the spin-angular space are simplified as follows: we use $\boldsymbol{\sigma}\cdot(\mathbf{L}Y_L^M)\chi_{\kappa'}^{\mu'} = \boldsymbol{\sigma}\cdot\mathbf{L}(Y_L^M\chi_{\kappa'}^{\mu'}) - Y_L^M\boldsymbol{\sigma}\cdot\mathbf{L}\chi_{\kappa'}^{\mu'}$ where, for clarity, parentheses are inserted to indicate the functions on which $\mathbf{L}$ operates. Since $\boldsymbol{\sigma}\cdot\mathbf{L}$ is hermitian the application of (5.11) gives

$$\begin{aligned}(-\kappa\mu|\boldsymbol{\sigma}\cdot\mathbf{L}Y_L^M|\kappa'\mu') &= (\boldsymbol{\sigma}\cdot\mathbf{L}\chi_{-\kappa}^{\mu}|Y_L^M|\chi_{\kappa'}^{\mu'}) - (\chi_{-\kappa}^{\mu}|Y_L^M|\boldsymbol{\sigma}\cdot\mathbf{L}\chi_{\kappa'}^{\mu'}) \\ &= (\kappa+\kappa')(-\kappa\mu|Y_L^M|\kappa'\mu') \quad (5.18)\end{aligned}$$

To obtain the second matrix element in (5.17) we have only to change the signs of κ and κ'. Thus

$$\begin{aligned}(\kappa\mu|\boldsymbol{\sigma}\cdot\mathbf{L}Y_L^M|-\kappa'\mu') &= -(\kappa+\kappa')(\kappa\mu|Y_L^M|-\kappa'\mu') \\ &= -(\kappa+\kappa')(-\kappa\mu|Y_L^M|\kappa'\mu') \quad (5.18')\end{aligned}$$

where in the last step (5.12) and the hermitian property of σ_r are used together with the result $\sigma_r^2 = 1$.

This shows that only one spin-angular matrix element is involved. Its evaluation proceeds as follows: We consider

$$(\chi_{-\kappa}^{\mu}, \chi_{\kappa'}^{\mu'}) = \sum_{\tau\tau'} C(\bar{l}\tfrac{1}{2}j; \mu-\tau, \tau)\, C(l'\tfrac{1}{2}j'; \mu'-\tau', \tau')(\chi_{\frac{1}{2}}^{\tau}, \chi_{\frac{1}{2}}^{\tau'})\, Y_{\bar{l}}^{\mu-\tau *}\, Y_{l'}^{\mu'-\tau'}$$

where the scalar product does *not* imply integration over $\mathbf{r}$. Of course

$$(\chi_{\frac{1}{2}}^{\tau}, \chi_{\frac{1}{2}}^{\tau'}) = \delta_{\tau\tau'}$$

and the product of the two spherical harmonics is expanded according to (2.32). The result is

$$(\chi^{\mu}_{-\kappa}, \chi^{\mu'}_{\kappa'}) = \sum_{\nu} \sqrt{\frac{(2\bar{l}+1)(2l'+1)}{4\pi(2\nu+1)}}\, C(\bar{l}l'\nu; 00)\, Y^{\mu'-\mu}_{\nu}\, \mathcal{S}_{\nu}$$

where

$$\mathcal{S}_{\nu} = \sum_{\tau} (-)^{\mu-\tau}\, C(\bar{l}\tfrac{1}{2}j, \mu-\tau, \tau)\, C(l'\tfrac{1}{2}j'; \mu'-\tau, \tau)\, C(\bar{l}l'\nu; -\mu+\tau, \mu'-\tau)$$

This sum is evaluated by the same procedure as was followed in sec. 11. The result is

$$\mathcal{S}_{\nu} = (-)^{l'+\bar{l}+\nu+\mu+\frac{1}{2}} \sqrt{(2j+1)(2j'+1)}\, C(jj'\nu; -\mu, \mu')\, W(j\bar{l}j'l'; \tfrac{1}{2}\nu) \tag{5.19}$$

The spin angular matrix element is then [7]

$$(-\kappa\mu|\, Y^{M}_{L}\, |\kappa'\mu') = (-)^{M} \sqrt{\frac{(2\bar{l}+1)(2l'+1)}{4\pi(2L+1)}}\, C(\bar{l}l'L; 00)\, \mathcal{S}_{L}\, \delta_{\mu,\, \mu'+M} \tag{5.20}$$

The selection rules are contained in the coefficient $\mathcal{S}_L$ and in the C-coefficient of (5.20). These give the triangular conditions $\Delta(jj'L)$ and $\Delta(\bar{l}l'L)$. In addition $\bar{l} + l' + L =$ even integer or $l_{\kappa} + l_{\kappa'} + L =$ odd integer. These are the selection rules referred to in sec. 26.

The summation $\mathfrak{S}$ in (5.4) is simply the operation of summing over j, μ, μ' and averaging over M. This is equivalent to summing over final states and averaging over initial states with a fixed M.[8] Applied to $\mathcal{S}_L^2$ this procedure gives

$$\frac{1}{2L+1} \sum_{\mu\mu' M j} \mathcal{S}_L^2 = \sum_{j} (2j+1)(2j'+1)\, W^2(j\bar{l}j'l'; \tfrac{1}{2}L)$$

It is this averaging process which shows that for a mixture of electric and magnetic multipoles there is no interference term and the intensities

[7] Since $(-)^{\mu+\frac{1}{2}+M}\, C(jj'L; -\mu, \mu') = \sqrt{(2L+1)/(2j+1)}\, (-)^{L-j-\frac{1}{2}}\, C(j'Lj; \mu'M)$ it is seen that (5.20) is in the form required by the Eckart theorem; cf. (2.79).

[8] Actually N_e is proportional to

$$\Sigma\, [C(J_f J_i L; -m, m')\, C(jj'L; -\mu, \mu')]^2$$

where J_i, J_f and m', m refer to the initial and final nuclear states. Since $\mu - \mu' = M = m' - m$ and the summation is over m, m' as well as μ, μ', the projection quantum number M must be fixed in the μ, μ' sum. The result of averaging over μ', summing over μ, is independent of M, and the sums over electronic and nuclear projection quantum numbers are effectively decoupled.

of the corresponding conversion electrons are additive. This follows since, for a given nuclear transition with specified parity, L must differ by 1 unit in the electric case as compared with the magnetic. The vanishing of the cross term is a consequence of the orthogonality of the C-coefficients. An interference term would arise if the direction of the conversion electron were observed relative to some physically defined direction; Biedenharn and Rose (53).

Combining these results the internal conversion coefficient for magnetic 2^L pole radiation is

$$\alpha(ML) = \frac{\pi\alpha k(2j'+1)(2l'+1)}{L(L+1)(2L+1)} \sum_j (2j+1)(2\bar{l}+1)(\kappa+\kappa')^2$$

$$\times\, C^2(\bar{l}l'L; 00)\, W^2(j\bar{l}j'l'; \tfrac{1}{2}L)\,|R_1 + R_2|^2 \quad (5.21)$$

The values of the Racah coefficients can be obtained from Table BI of Appendix B. The explicit form for the C-coefficient occurring in (5.21) is also given there.

As an example we consider the initial state to be the K-shell, or any other shell with $\kappa' = -1$. The only difference, arising from the principal quantum number which distinguishes these various possible initial states with the same κ', is in the radial integrals. The $\kappa' = -1$ corresponds to $l' = 0$ and $j' = \frac{1}{2}$. The possible final states are characterized by $j = L + \frac{1}{2}$ and $L - \frac{1}{2}$ or $\kappa = L + 1$ and $-L$ respectively. For both cases $\bar{l} = L$. The C-coefficient in (5.21) is then unity. In this simple case

$$W^2(j\bar{l}\tfrac{1}{2}0; \tfrac{1}{2}L) = \frac{1}{2(2L+1)}$$

and

$$\alpha(ML) = \frac{2\pi\alpha k}{2L+1}\{L|R_1 + R_2|^2_{\kappa=L+1} + (L+1)|R_1 + R_2|^2_{\kappa=-L}\} \quad (5.22)$$

The evaluation of the radial integrals for the Coulomb field and for the K-shell has been carried out by Rose, Goertzel, Spinrad, Harr, and Strong (51) where numerical results for the K-shell conversion coefficients may be found.

In evaluating the electric multipole conversion coefficient the procedure is much the same. It is most convenient to express the outgoing wave multipole fields in the following way:

$$\mathbf{B}_L^M(e) = \sqrt{\frac{2}{\pi}\frac{1}{L(L+1)}}\, h_{L-1}(r\nabla + L\mathbf{r})Y_L^M \tag{5.23a}$$

$$V_L^M(e) = i\sqrt{\frac{2}{\pi}\frac{L}{(L+1)}}\, h_L\, Y_L^M \tag{5.23b}$$

That (5.23a) is identical with (5.5a) is easily seen by application of the gradient formula (2.57) and the coupling rule (2.32). The evaluation of the spin-angular matrix elements is facilitated by the use of the identity

$$r\sigma\cdot\nabla = \sigma_r\left(r\frac{\partial}{\partial r} - \boldsymbol{\sigma}\cdot\mathbf{L}\right) \tag{5.24}$$

Details of the calculation are very much like those performed in obtaining the intensity for the emission of magnetic multipole radiation by a nucleus, sec. 30.

The selection rules are easily found to be $\Delta(jj'L)$, $\Delta(ll'L)$, and $l + l' + L =$ even integer. The conversion coefficient for an initial state with arbitrary κ' is

$$\alpha(EL) = \frac{\pi\alpha kL(2j'+1)(2l'+1)}{(L+1)(2L+1)}\sum_\kappa (2l+1)(2j+1)\, C^2(ll'L;00)$$
$$\times W^2(jlj'l';\tfrac{1}{2}L)\left|\frac{\kappa'-\kappa}{L}(R_5+R_6) + R_6 - R_5 + R_3 + R_4\right|^2$$

The allowed values of κ for electric conversion are the negatives of those for magnetic conversion and, for a given initial state and $|\kappa|$, the quantity $\bar{l}$ which appears in (5.21) is equal to the quantity l appearing above. For $\kappa' = -1$ the electric conversion coefficient is

$$\alpha(EL) = \frac{2\pi\alpha kL}{(L+1)(2L+1)}\left\{(L+1)\left|R_3 + R_4 + 2R_6\right|^2_{\kappa=-L-1}\right.$$
$$\left. + L\left|R_3 + R_4 - \left(2 + \frac{1}{L}\right)R_5 - \frac{R_6}{L}\right|^2_{\kappa=L}\right\} \tag{5.25}$$

Here the radial integrals are

$$R_3 = \int_0^\infty f_\kappa\, h_L\, f_{\kappa'}\, r^2\, dr \qquad R_4 = \int_0^\infty g_\kappa\, h_L\, g_{\kappa'}\, r^2\, dr$$

$$R_5 = \int_0^\infty f_\kappa\, h_{L-1}\, g_{\kappa'}\, r^2\, dr \qquad R_6 = \int_0^\infty g_\kappa\, h_{L-1}\, f_{\kappa'}\, r^2\, dr$$

Numerical results for the K-shell are to be found in the reference cited above.

VI. EMISSION OF GAMMA RADIATION

28. FORMULATION OF THE PROBLEM

The theory of gamma-ray emission from excited nuclear states is of central importance in nuclear physics. Because of some uncertainty with regard to the nuclear forces it is not possible to provide a complete description of this process; cf. sec. 23. Nevertheless, the results that can be obtained are of considerable utility. The motivation here is concerned with the gamma-ray-emission problem as an application of the principles and results presented in foregoing chapters, and a complete discussion of the applications of the theory to experimental results will not be attempted.[1] However, it may be noted at this point that one of the striking properties of nuclear states—that the lifetime of the state can become very large if all transitions to lower-lying states involve small energy changes and large changes of angular momentum—is readily understood in terms of the theory. Such long-lived states, known as isomeric states, must necessarily have low excitation, and so comparatively few radiative transitions are possible. In fact, isomeric states will generally be found to coincide with the first (or possibly second) excited state. For states of appreciably greater excitation, where several levels exist at lower energy, the dominant mode of emission will be *via* low-order (dipole or quadrupole) multipole radiation.

The transition probability, quanta per second, is

$$\frac{1}{\tau} = N_q = \frac{2\pi}{\hbar}\mathfrak{S}|\mathfrak{H}_{fi}|^2 N(E) \tag{6.1}$$

in ordinary units. Here τ is the mean life, $\mathfrak{H}_{fi}$ is the matrix element which was denoted by $\mathfrak{H}_{fi}^{(1)}$ in Chapter IV, $N(E)$ is the number of final states available per unit energy. For quantization in a box of volume

[1] See, for example, Moszkowski (53) or Stech (52). It should be emphasized that, in contrast to the problem of internal conversion, the description of gamma-ray emission by nuclei depends upon the explicit use of a model (at least for magnetic multipole emission, see below) and that the validity of the physical assumptions on which this model is based is somewhat open to question. For the internal-conversion process the only model utilized is the well-justified Dirac electron theory.

V, see sec. 19, the number of quanta per unit energy interval traveling in the solid angle $d\Omega$ is

$$N(E) = \frac{p^2\, dp/dW}{(2\pi\hbar)^3} V\, d\Omega$$

where the momentum of the radiation is $p = \hbar\omega/c = W/c$. Hence

$$N(E) = \frac{\omega^2 V}{8\pi^3 \hbar c^3} d\Omega \tag{6.2}$$

The vector potential of the plane wave emitted is, cf. (3.32),

$$\mathbf{A} = \sqrt{2\pi\hbar c^2/\omega V}\, \mathbf{u}_P\, e^{i\mathbf{k}\cdot\mathbf{r}} \tag{6.3}$$

where $\mathbf{u}_P$ is a unit polarization vector for the polarization state P. In (6.1) the summation $\mathfrak{S}$ is over all propagation directions and polarization states and, in addition, involves a summation (denoted by $\mathfrak{S}'$) over magnetic substates. Thus,

$$\frac{1}{\tau} = \frac{\omega}{2\pi\hbar c} \mathfrak{S}' \sum_P \int |\mathfrak{H}_{fi}(\mathbf{A}_1)|^2\, d\Omega \tag{6.4}$$

where

$$\mathbf{A}_1 = \mathbf{u}_P\, e^{i\mathbf{k}\cdot\mathbf{r}} \tag{6.3'}$$

The plane wave (6.3) is, of course, representable as a superposition of multipoles. In the emission of a gamma ray between nuclear states of specified angular momentum and parity, one or at most two terms will be relevant. All other terms either violate the selection rules or are negligible in the long-wavelength limit as explained in sec. 25; see also equations 6.22 and 6.30 below. For this reason it is essential to expand $\mathbf{A}_1$ into a multipole series. For this purpose we use a basis of circularly polarized waves and

$$\mathbf{u}_P = \frac{1}{\sqrt{2}} (\mathbf{u}_1 + iP\mathbf{u}_2) \tag{6.3''}$$

where $\mathbf{u}_1$ and $\mathbf{u}_2$ are (real) unit vectors such that $\mathbf{u}_1$, $\mathbf{u}_2$, and $\mathbf{k}/k$ form a right-handed orthogonal cartesian coordinate system. In (6.4) and (6.3′) the polarization index $P = \pm 1$ with $P = 1$ corresponding to left circularly polarized waves and $P = -1$ to right circularly polarized waves.

We first consider a plane wave propagating along the z-axis. Thus, $\mathbf{u}_1 = \mathbf{e}_x$ and $\mathbf{u}_2 = \mathbf{e}_y$. Therefore $\mathbf{u}_P = -P\, \boldsymbol{\xi}_P$. Then the well-known Rayleigh expansion gives

$$\mathbf{A}_1^0 = -P\, \boldsymbol{\xi}_P \sqrt{4\pi} \sum_{l=0}^{\infty} i^l \sqrt{2l+1}\, Y_l^0(\cos\vartheta)\, j_l(kr) \tag{6.5}$$

where $z = r\cos\vartheta$. The superscript in $\mathbf{A}_1^0$ indicates $k = k_z$. The series (6.5) can be expressed in terms of multipoles by inverting (2.43) by means of (2.18). Thus

$$Y_l^m\,\boldsymbol{\xi}_{m'} = \sum_L C(1lL;\,m'm)\,\mathbf{T}_{Ll}^{m+m'} \tag{6.6}$$

Therefore

$$\mathbf{A}_1^0 = -P\sqrt{4\pi}\sum_{l=0}^{\infty} i^l\sqrt{2l+1}\,j_l\sum_L C(1lL;\,P0)\,\mathbf{T}_{Ll}^P$$

In this sum $L = l,\ l \pm 1$. Writing out the three terms explicitly with the aid of

$$C(1ll;\,P0) = \frac{P}{\sqrt{2}}$$

$$C(1l\,l{+}1;\,P0) = \sqrt{\frac{l+2}{2(2l+1)}}$$

$$C(1l\,l{-}1;\,P0) = \sqrt{\frac{l-1}{2(2l+1)}}\,(1-\delta_{l0})$$

we have

$$\mathbf{A}_1^0 = -P\sqrt{2\pi}\sum_{l=0}^{\infty} i^l\sqrt{2l+1}\,j_l \times\left\{P\,\mathbf{T}_{l,l}^P + \sqrt{\frac{l+2}{2l+1}}\,\mathbf{T}_{l+1,l}^P + \sqrt{\frac{l-1}{2l+1}}\,\mathbf{T}_{l-1,l}^P\right\}$$

We now introduce $f_L = \sqrt{2/\pi}\,j_L$ and set $l + 1 = L$ in the second sum, $l - 1 = L$ in the third, and $l = L$ in the first. Since $\mathbf{T}_{L,L-1} = \mathbf{T}_{LL} = 0$ for $L = 0$, the plane wave $\mathbf{A}_1^0$ becomes

$$\mathbf{A}_1^0 = \pi\sum_{L=1}^{\infty} i^L\sqrt{2L+1}\,\{\mathbf{A}_L^P(m) + iP\mathbf{A}_L^P(e)\} \tag{6.7}$$

Of course, the potentials are in the solenoidal gauge. To obtain the expansion of the plane wave propagating in an arbitrary direction $\mathbf{k}$, with polar and azimuth angles θ, φ, the result (6.7) is rotated with Euler angles $\alpha = \phi$, $\beta = \theta$, $\gamma = 0$. Thus

$$\mathbf{A}_1 = \pi\sum_{L=1}^{\infty}\sum_{M=-L}^{L} i^L\sqrt{2L+1}\,D_{MP}^L(\varphi\theta 0)\{\mathbf{A}_L^M(m) + iP\mathbf{A}_L^M(e)\} \tag{6.8}$$

This is the form in which this expansion was obtained by Goertzel (46). The derivation given here follows the procedure of Biedenharn and

Rose (53). Of course, the same expansion applies for the field strengths. The occurrence of $\mathbf{A}_L^P$ in (6.7) shows that a photon may have angular-momentum components about its direction of propagation equal to ± 1 only.

For propagation in the direction $-\mathbf{k}$ the corresponding expansion is easily obtained from

$$D_{MP}^L(-\mathbf{k}_1) = (-)^L D_{M-P}^L(\mathbf{k}_1) \tag{6.9}$$

where $\mathbf{k}_1$, a unit vector in the direction of $\mathbf{k}$, collectively denotes the arguments of the D matrix. Thus,

$$\mathbf{u}_{-P}\, e^{-i\mathbf{k}\cdot\mathbf{r}} = \pi \sum_{LM} (-i)^L \sqrt{2L+1}\, D_{MP}^L(\mathbf{k}_1)\{\mathbf{A}_L^M(m) - iP\mathbf{A}_L^M(e)\} \tag{6.10}$$

Properly speaking, this is the appropriate potential for emission although, since an integration over $\mathbf{k}_1$ and a sum over P is performed, either (6.8) or (6.10) may be used.

From the results of sec. 16 it follows that $\mathbf{A}_L^M(m)\cdot\mathbf{A}_L^M(e) = 0$ and that in the wave zone these two vector potentials are in phase and are of equal magnitude. Hence, in this case, the fields represented by $\mathbf{A}_L^M(m) \pm i\mathbf{A}_L^M(e)$ represent circularly polarized waves; cf. Kramers (43).

29. EMISSION OF ELECTRIC MULTIPOLE RADIATION

In sec. 23 some discussion was given to the question of the construction of a gauge-invariant hamiltonian, and it was stated that without a knowledge of nuclear forces, unhappily not now available, this construction was not possible without ambiguity. However, in the limit of long wavelengths the problem of the nuclear forces is irrelevant as far as the emission of electric multipoles is concerned; Siegert (37) and Sachs and Austern (51).

To demonstrate the validity of this interaction-independence of the electric multipole coupling we first remark that the vector potential $\mathbf{A}_L^M(e)$ can be decomposed into two parts, one of which is irrotational. Of course, this can be done in more than one way. For example, equation 3.11 is such a decomposition. Another procedure [Sachs and Austern (51)] is to use the identity

$$\mathbf{A}_1 = \mathbf{u}_{-P}\, e^{-i\mathbf{k}\cdot\mathbf{r}} \equiv \nabla S' + i\mathbf{r} \times (\mathbf{k} \times \mathbf{S}') \tag{6.11}$$

where

$$S' = \mathbf{r}\cdot\int_0^r \mathbf{A}_1(\mathbf{r}')\, dr' \tag{6.11a}$$

with the integration taken along the straight line from the origin to $\mathbf{r}$;

$$\mathbf{S}' = \frac{1}{r^2} \int_0^r r' \, \mathbf{A}(\mathbf{r}') \, dr' \tag{6.11b}$$

with the same path of integration. In the long-wavelength limit the two decompositions (3.11) and (6.11) are identical. We use (3.11) in the following. Then writing $\mathbf{A}_1 = \mathbf{A}_1(e) + \mathbf{A}_1(m)$

$$\mathbf{A}_1(e) = \nabla S + \mathbf{A}_1'$$

where

$$S = \frac{\pi P}{k} \sum_{LM} (-i)^{L+1} \sqrt{\frac{2L+1}{L(L+1)}} \, D^L_{MP}(\mathbf{k}_1) \left(1 + r\frac{d}{dr}\right) f_L \, Y^M_L \tag{6.12}$$

and

$$\mathbf{A}_1' = \pi P k \sum_{LM} (-i)^{L+1} \sqrt{\frac{2L+1}{L(L+1)}} \, D^L_{MP}(\mathbf{k}_1) f_L \, \mathbf{r} \, Y^M_L \tag{6.13}$$

It should be noted that S is not a gauge function because $(1 + r\,d/dr)$ does not commute with the radial part of the Laplace operator. Thus, while the irrotational part of $\mathbf{A}_1$ does not contribute to the magnetic field it does give rise to an electric field. It may also be recalled, sec. 18, that in the limit $kr \ll 1$ the electric field is dominant for the electric multipole. One may therefore expect that in the long-wavelength limit only the irrotational part of $\mathbf{A}_1$ is of importance. This is now shown to be the case by an explicit evaluation.

From the gradient formula 2.58 we obtain

$$\begin{aligned} \nabla S = \frac{\pi P}{kr} \sum_{LM} \frac{(-i)^{L+1}}{\sqrt{L(L+1)}} D^L_{MP}(\mathbf{k}_1) \\ \times \left\{ \sqrt{L+1} \, \mathbf{T}^M_{L,L+1} \left[-(L^2 - k^2r^2) f_L + Lr \frac{df_L}{dr} \right] \right. \\ \left. + \sqrt{L} \, \mathbf{T}^M_{L,L-1} \left[(L+1)^2 f_L - k^2 r^2 f_L + (L+1) r \frac{df_L}{dr} \right] \right\} \end{aligned} \tag{6.14}$$

and from (2.32), after using

$$\mathbf{r} = r \sqrt{\frac{4\pi}{3}} \sum_{\mu} (-)^{\mu} Y^{\mu}_1 \, \boldsymbol{\xi}_{-\mu}$$

we find

$$\mathbf{A}_1' = -\pi P k r \sum_{LM} \frac{(-i)^{L+1}}{\sqrt{L(L+1)}} D^L_{MP}(\mathbf{k}_1) f_L$$

$$\times \{\sqrt{L+1}\, \mathbf{T}^M_{L,L+1} - \sqrt{L}\, \mathbf{T}^M_{L,L-1}\} \quad (6.15)$$

The radial functions in the square brackets in (6.14) are, for $kr \ll 1$,

$$Lr\frac{df_L}{dr} - (L^2 - k^2r^2)f_L \sim O(kr)^{L+2}$$

$$(L+1)r\frac{df_L}{dr} + (L+1)^2 f_L - k^2r^2 f_L \sim \sqrt{\frac{2}{\pi}}\frac{L+1}{(2L-1)!!}(kr)^L$$

On the other hand $|\mathbf{A}_1'| \sim (kr)^{L+1}$, which is smaller than the second term in ∇S by a factor of order $(kr)^2$. Therefore, for the electric multipole case, we can take

$$\mathbf{A}_1(e) = \nabla S \quad (6.16)$$

where

$$S \cong \frac{\sqrt{2\pi}P}{k} \sum_{LM} \frac{(-i)^{L+1}}{(2L+1)!!}$$

$$\times \sqrt{\frac{(2L+1)(L+1)}{L}}\, D^L_{MP}(\mathbf{k}_1)(kr)^L\, Y^M_L \quad (6.17)$$

The second step in the argument is to use the principle of gauge invariance. Inasmuch as the hamiltonian must be gauge invariant it follows (cf. 4.20) that

$$\mathfrak{H}(\mathbf{A} + \nabla S) = e^{\Lambda}\, \mathfrak{H}(\mathbf{A})\, e^{-\Lambda}$$

where $\mathbf{A}$ is any vector potential and

$$\Lambda = \frac{i}{\hbar c} \sum_l e_l S(\mathbf{r}_l) \quad (6.18)$$

while $\mathbf{r}_l$ is the position of the lth nucleon with charge e_l. With the expansion (4.22)

$$\mathfrak{H}(0) + \mathfrak{H}^{(1)}(\mathbf{A} + \nabla S) + \cdots = e^{\Lambda}\{\mathfrak{H}(0) + \mathfrak{H}^{(1)}(\mathbf{A}) + \cdots\}e^{-\Lambda}$$

$$= \mathfrak{H}(0) + [\Lambda, \mathfrak{H}(0)] + \mathfrak{H}^{(1)}(\mathbf{A}) + \cdots$$

where the expansion has been carried to first-order terms on each side.

Again, the square bracket is the commutator. Since $\mathfrak{H}^{(1)}$ is a linear operator

$$\mathfrak{H}^{(1)}(A + \nabla S) = \mathfrak{H}^{(1)}(\mathbf{A}) + \mathfrak{H}^{(1)}(\nabla S)$$

it follows that [cf. Sachs and Austern (51)]

$$\mathfrak{H}^{(1)}(\nabla S) = [\Lambda, \mathfrak{H}(0)] \tag{6.18'}$$

From (6.16) we find for the required matrix element

$$\mathfrak{H}_{fi} = (f|\mathfrak{H}^{(1)}(\nabla S)|i) = (f|[\Lambda, \mathfrak{H}(0)]|i) = (W_i - W_f)(f|\Lambda|i)$$

and W_i and W_f are the nuclear energy values for initial and final states, respectively. Since we are dealing with the case of emission, this is

$$\mathfrak{H}_{fi} = \hbar ck(f|\Lambda|i) \tag{6.19}$$

Equation 6.19 is a formal expression of the Siegert theorem according to which the electric multipole emission operator is $\hbar ck\Lambda$, see (6.17) and (6.18), independent of the nature of the nuclear interactions; cf. Brennan and Sachs (52).

To evaluate the lifetime for the electric multipole case we adopt the *j-j* coupling model [Mayer (50)] according to which the nuclear wave functions are to be constructed from single-particle wave functions ψ_j^μ, where

$$\psi_j^\mu = \mathcal{R}(r)\, \chi_\kappa^\mu \tag{6.20}$$

[cf. (5.10)] are eigenfunctions of $\mathbf{j}^2$, j_z, and $\mathbf{L}^2$ with eigenvalues $j(j+1)$, μ, and $l(l+1)$. In (6.20), $\mathcal{R}(r)$ is a radial wave function. We consider the case of a single nucleon configuration. Then for a 2^L pole

$$\mathfrak{H}_{fi} = (-i)^L e \sqrt{\frac{2\pi(L+1)(2L+1)}{L}} \sum_M \frac{D^L_{MP}(\mathbf{k}_1)}{(2L+1)!!} P(kR)^L \times (\chi_\kappa^\mu | Y_L^M | \chi_{\kappa'}^{\mu'}) \mathfrak{M}_L \tag{6.21}$$

where κ, μ denote the final state and κ', μ' denote the initial state. Here $\mathfrak{M}_L$ is a (real) radial matrix element

$$\mathfrak{M}_L = \int \mathcal{R}_f \left(\frac{r}{R}\right)^L \mathcal{R}_i\, r^2\, dr \tag{6.21'}$$

The spin-angular matrix element was evaluated in sec. 27, equation 5.20. We use this result, averaging over the initial substates and summing over the final substates, and note that the integration over $\mathbf{k}_1$ is carried out simply [cf. Wigner (31)] by

$$\int d\Omega\,|D^L_{MP}(\mathbf{k}_1)|^2 = \frac{4\pi}{2L+1}$$

so that the polarization sum merely yields a factor 2.

The result is

$$\frac{1}{\tau} = 2\,\frac{L+1}{L}\,\frac{(2l+1)(2j+1)(2l'+1)}{[(2L+1)!!]^2} \times [C(ll'L;00)\,W(jlj'l';\tfrac{1}{2}L)]^2\,\omega\,\frac{e^2}{\hbar c}\,(kR)^{2L}\mathfrak{M}_L^2 \quad (6.22)$$

This is just the result obtained by Moszkowski (53) when the spin-angular integrals appearing in his work are evaluated as above. Again, numerical results are obtained by using the results given in Appendix B.

The selection rules $\Delta(jj'L)$, $\Delta(ll'L)$, and $l + l' + L =$ even integer will be noted. The long lifetime of nuclear isomers is associated with small k and large L and arises primarily from the retardation parameter $(kR)^{2L}$. The selection rules for electric radiation will be discussed in greater detail in sec. 31.

30. EMISSION OF MAGNETIC MULTIPOLE RADIATION

In order to calculate the mean lifetime for the emission of magnetic multipole radiation it is necessary to make some assumption concerning the nuclear forces. We consider a single-particle configuration, that is, one nucleon outside a closed shell subject to an ordinary potential $V(r)$, due to the remaining nucleons. The hamiltonian for a single proton is

$$\mathfrak{H} = \frac{1}{2M_p}(\mathbf{p} - e\mathbf{A})^2 + V(r) - \mu_p\frac{e\hbar}{2M_pc}\,\boldsymbol{\sigma}\cdot\mathbf{H} \quad (6.23)$$

where $\mu_p = 2.79$ is the proton magnetic moment in units of the nuclear Bohr magneton $e\hbar/2M_pc$. We use M_p for the proton mass to avoid confusion with M, the projection quantum number of the radiation. Equation 6.4 gives the reciprocal mean lifetime with

$$\mathfrak{H}_{fi} = -(e/M_pc)(\mathbf{A}_1\cdot\mathbf{p} + \tfrac{1}{2}\mu_p\hbar\,\boldsymbol{\sigma}\cdot\mathbf{H}_1) \quad (6.24)$$

where $\mathbf{A}_1$ is given by (6.8) and $\mathbf{H}_1 = \text{curl}\,\mathbf{A}_1$. The reciprocal mean lifetime for the 2^L magnetic pole may then be written in the form

$$\frac{1}{\tau} = 4\pi^2\frac{e^2}{\hbar c}\left(\frac{\hbar}{M_pc}\right)^2\omega\,\mathfrak{S}'\,|(f|-\mathbf{A}_L^M(m)\cdot\nabla + \tfrac{1}{2}k\mu_p\,\boldsymbol{\sigma}\cdot\mathbf{A}_L^M(e)\,|i)|^2 \quad (6.25)$$

where use has been made of $\mathbf{H}_L^M(m) = ik\mathbf{A}_L^M(e)$ and $\mathbf{A}_L^M(e)$ is therefore in the solenoidal gauge. The wave functions ψ_f and ψ_i have the form (6.20).

From (2.63) and (2.43) we find

$$-\mathbf{A}_L^M(m)\cdot\nabla = f_L \mathbf{T}_{LL}^M\cdot\nabla = f_L \sum_\mu C(1LL;\, -\mu, \mu+M)\, Y_L^{\mu+M}\, \nabla_{-\mu}$$

The matrix elements of this operator (which is, incidentally, an irreducible tensor of rank L) are obtained by a straightforward but lengthy application of the Racah algebra, sec. 11. For the $\nabla_{-\mu}$ operator acting on ψ_i we use the gradient formula 2.57. The result is

$$\begin{aligned}(f|-\mathbf{A}_L^M(m)\cdot\nabla|i) &= (-)^{l+\frac{1}{2}+\mu'} \\ &\times \sqrt{\frac{(2L+1)(2l+1)(2j+1)(2j'+1)}{4\pi}}\,(kR)^{L-1}\,k \\ &\times \sqrt{\frac{2}{\pi}}\frac{1}{(2L+1)!!}\,C(jj'L;\,-\mu\mu')\,W(ljl'j';\,\tfrac{1}{2}L) \\ &\times \{N_L^-\sqrt{l'+1}\,C(lL\,l'+1;\,00)\,W(LL\,l'+1\,l';\,1l) \\ &\qquad - N_L^+\sqrt{l'}\,C(lL\,l'-1;\,00)\,W(LL\,l'-1\,l';\,1l)\}\end{aligned} \tag{6.26}$$

In (6.26) the radial integrals are

$$N_L^- = \frac{1}{R^{L-1}}\int r^{L+2}\,\mathcal{R}_f\left(\frac{d}{dr}-\frac{l'}{r}\right)\mathcal{R}_i\,dr \tag{6.26a}$$

$$N_L^+ = \frac{1}{R^{L-1}}\int r^{L+2}\,\mathcal{R}_f\left(\frac{d}{dr}+\frac{l'+1}{r}\right)\mathcal{R}_i\,dr \tag{6.26b}$$

To evaluate the matrix element of the second operator in (6.25) we use (3.11) for $\mathbf{A}_L^M(e)$. With (5.24) we obtain

$$\boldsymbol{\sigma}\cdot\mathbf{A}_L^M(e) = \frac{\sigma_r}{\sqrt{L(L+1)}} \times \left\{kr\,f_L\,Y_L^M + \frac{1}{kr}\left(r\frac{\partial}{\partial r} - \boldsymbol{\sigma}\cdot\mathbf{L}\right)Y_L^M\left(1+r\frac{d}{dr}\right)f_L\right\}$$

By a procedure exactly like that followed in sec. 27 we find for the matrix element of this operator

$$(f|\boldsymbol{\sigma}\cdot\mathbf{A}_L^M(e)|i) = -\frac{1}{\sqrt{L(L+1)}}(-\kappa\mu|Y_L^M|\kappa'\mu')$$
$$\times\left\{(\mathcal{R}_f|krf_L|\mathcal{R}_i) + \left(\mathcal{R}_f\left|\frac{1}{k}\frac{d}{dr}\left(1+r\frac{d}{dr}\right)f_L\right|\mathcal{R}_i\right)\right.$$
$$\left. - (\kappa+\kappa')\left(\mathcal{R}_f\left|\frac{1}{kr}\left(1+r\frac{d}{dr}\right)f_L\right|\mathcal{R}_i\right)\right\}$$

The radial integrals in the retardation limit are

$$(\mathcal{R}_f|krf_L|\mathcal{R}_i) \cong \sqrt{\frac{2}{\pi}}\frac{(kR)^{L+1}}{(2L+1)!!}\mathfrak{M}_{L+1}$$

$$\left(\mathcal{R}_f\left|\frac{1}{k}\frac{d}{dr}\left(1+r\frac{d}{dr}\right)f_L\right|\mathcal{R}_i\right) \cong \sqrt{\frac{2}{\pi}}\frac{L(L+1)}{(2L+1)!!}(kR)^{L-1}\,\mathfrak{M}_{L-1}$$

$$\left(\mathcal{R}_f\left|\frac{1}{kr}\left(1+r\frac{d}{dr}\right)f_L\right|\mathcal{R}_i\right) \cong \sqrt{\frac{2}{\pi}}\frac{L+1}{(2L+1)!!}(kR)^{L-1}\,\mathfrak{M}_{L-1}$$

where $\mathfrak{M}_{L\pm1}$ is defined by (6.21′). Consequently only the second and third terms are important. This is simply a verification of the general result of sec. 29. The matrix element of the second term in (6.25) then becomes

$$(f|k\mu_p\boldsymbol{\sigma}\cdot\mathbf{A}_L^M(e)|i) = \sqrt{\frac{2}{\pi}\frac{L+1}{L}}\frac{\kappa+\kappa'-L}{(2L+1)!!}k\mu_p\,(kR)^{L-1}\,\mathfrak{M}_{L-1}$$
$$\times(-\kappa\mu|Y_L^M|\kappa'\mu') \quad (6.27)$$

and the spin-angular matrix element is given by (5.20).

The radial matrix elements which occur in (6.26) can be transformed to the form $\mathfrak{M}_{L\pm1}$ by using the radial-wave equations

$$\frac{d^2\mathcal{R}_i}{dr^2} + \frac{2}{r}\frac{d\mathcal{R}_i}{dr} + \left[\frac{2M}{\hbar^2}(W_i - V) - \frac{l'(l'+1)}{r^2}\right]\mathcal{R}_i = 0 \quad (6.28a)$$

$$\frac{d^2\mathcal{R}_f}{dr^2} + \frac{2}{r}\frac{d\mathcal{R}_f}{dr^2} + \left[\frac{2M}{\hbar^2}(W_f - V) - \frac{l(l+1)}{r^2}\right]\mathcal{R}_f = 0 \quad (6.28b)$$

Multiplying the left-hand side of (6.28b) by $r^{L+3}\,\mathcal{R}_i$ and subtracting from the product of $r^{L+3}\,\mathcal{R}_f$ with the left side of (6.28a) and then integrating over r we obtain

$$(L+1)N_L^- = \tfrac{1}{2}(l - l' - L - 1)(l + l' + L + 2)\mathfrak{M}_{L-1} + \frac{MckR^2}{\hbar}\mathfrak{M}_{L+1} \tag{6.29a}$$

$$(L+1)N_L^+ = \tfrac{1}{2}(l - l' + L + 1)(l + l' - L)\mathfrak{M}_{L-1} + \frac{MckR^2}{\hbar}\mathfrak{M}_{L+1} \tag{6.29b}$$

It will be noted that the second terms in (6.29) are not necessarily small compared to the first terms. Thus $\mathfrak{M}_{L+1} \sim \mathfrak{M}_{L-1}$, and the ratio of second to first terms in (6.29) is of order

$$(M_p ckR^2/\hbar) \sim \tfrac{1}{20}(\hbar\omega)_{\text{Mev}}\, A^{2/3}$$

where A is here the mass number of the emitting nucleus. This quantity, which is the product of the small retardation parameter $(kR)^2$ and the large momentum ratio $M_pc/\hbar k$, is of order 0.1 for 200-kev radiation and a light nucleus ($A \sim 30$). But for 1-Mev radiation and $A \sim 200$, the ratio may be of order unity or larger. Nevertheless, the $\mathfrak{M}_{L+1}$ terms do not appear in the final result since they enter with a coefficient proportional to

$$\sqrt{l'+1}\, C(lL\,l'{+}1;00)\, W(LL\,l'{+}1\,l';1l) - \sqrt{l'}\, C(lL\,l'{-}1;00)\, W(LL\,l'{-}1\,l';1l) \equiv 0$$

by (B.3) and Table BII of Appendix B. Since the selection rule derived from (6.26) requires $\Delta(lL\,l'{\pm}1)$ with $l + L + l' =$ odd integer, it is even possible for the first term in N_L^-, or in N_L^+, to vanish. They cannot vanish simultaneously, however.

The final result for the reciprocal mean lifetime is

$$\frac{1}{\tau} = 2\frac{e^2}{\hbar c}\,\omega\left(\frac{\hbar k}{M_pc}\right)^2 (kR)^{2(L-1)}\,\frac{(2j+1)(2L+1)}{[(2L+1)!!]^2}\,\mathfrak{M}_{L-1}^2$$
$$\times \{(2l'+1)\sqrt{(2L+1)(2l+1)(l'+1)}\; C(lL\,l'{+}1;00)$$
$$\times W(ljl'j';\tfrac{1}{2}L)\, W(LL\,l'{+}1\,l';1l) + \tfrac{1}{2}\mu_p(\kappa+\kappa'-L)$$
$$\times \sqrt{\frac{(L+1)(2\bar{l}+1)}{L}}\; C(\bar{l}Ll';00)\, W(\bar{l}jl'j';\tfrac{1}{2}L)\}^2 \tag{6.30}$$

Although this result appears in rather complicated form, numerical results (in terms of radial integrals) are obtained from it without difficulty by recourse to the tables of Appendix B. In detail, we consider the four possible types of transitions: (i) $j = l + \frac{1}{2}$ (that is, $\kappa < 0$) and $j' = l' + \frac{1}{2}(\kappa' < 0)$; (ii) $j = l - \frac{1}{2}(\kappa > 0)$ and $j' = l' - \frac{1}{2}(\kappa' > 0)$; (iii) $j = l + \frac{1}{2}$ and $j' = l' - \frac{1}{2}$; (iv) $j = l - \frac{1}{2}$ and $j' = l' + \frac{1}{2}$. Then we may write

$$\frac{1}{\tau} = \frac{1}{2}\frac{e^2}{\hbar c}\,\omega\left(\frac{\hbar k}{M_p c}\right)^2 (kR)^{2(L-1)}\,\frac{(2j+1)(2L+1)}{[(2L+1)!!]^2}\,\frac{C^2(lL\,l'{+}1;00)}{L(L+1)} \times B(1-\Lambda\mu_p)^2\,\mathfrak{M}_{L-1}^2 \qquad (6.30a)$$

and the constants B and Λ are

(i)

$$B = \frac{(l+l'+L+2)^2(l+l'+1-L)^2(L+l'-l+1)(L+l-l')}{(2l'+3)(2l'+2)(2l+2)}$$

$$\Lambda = \frac{-(L+1)}{l+l'-L+1} \qquad (6.30b)$$

(ii) $$B = \frac{\left\{\begin{array}{l}(l+l'+L+2)(l+l'+L+1)(l+L-l')\\ \times\,(l+l'-L)(l+l'-L+1)(l'+L-l+1)\end{array}\right\}}{2l'(2l'+3)2l}$$

$$\Lambda = \frac{(L+1)}{l+l'+L+1} \qquad (6.30c)$$

(iii) $$B = \frac{\left\{\begin{array}{l}(l+l'+L+2)(l-l'+L+1)(l'-l+L+1)\\ \times\,(l+l'-L+1)(L+l-l')(L-l+l')\end{array}\right\}}{2l'(2l'+3)(2l+2)}$$

$$\Lambda = \frac{(L+1)}{L-l+l'} \qquad (6.30d)$$

(iv)

$$B = \frac{(l+l'+L+2)(l'-l+L+1)^2(l-l'+L)^2(l-L+l'+1)}{(2l'+2)(2l'+3)2l}$$

$$\Lambda = \frac{(L+1)}{L-l'+l} \qquad (6.30e)$$

Similar results have been obtained by Sharp et al. (53).

In sec. 31 it will be seen that the cases of practical interest are

$$L = l - l' + 1 \qquad l \geq l'$$

and

$$L = l' - l + 1 \qquad l' \geq l$$

In these cases the C-coefficient appearing in (6.30a) takes the values

$$C(l\,l'-l+1\,l'+1;00) = \frac{(l'+1)!}{l!(l'-l+1)!}\sqrt{\frac{(2l)!(2l'-2l+2)!}{(2l'+2)!}}$$

$$C(l\,l-l'+1\,l'+1;00) = \frac{(-)^{l+l'}(l+1)!}{l'!(l-l')!}\sqrt{\frac{(2l-2l')!(2l')!2(2l'+3)}{(2l+3)!}}$$

31. SELECTION RULES AND RELATIVE INTENSITIES

The transition rates for electric and magnetic transitions, as given by (6.22) and (6.30), should be evaluated for the minimum permissible value of L. This minimum value of L is fixed by the selection rules. In all cases the triangular condition $\Delta(jj'L)$, expressing conservation of angular momentum, applies. For electric radiation one has, in addition, the triangular condition $\Delta(ll'L)$ with $L + \Delta l$ an even integer, where $\Delta l = |l - l'|$. For the four possible types of transitions described above, $\Delta j = |j - j'| = \Delta l + \epsilon$, where $\epsilon = 0, \pm 1$. For $\Delta j < \Delta l$ the minimum L is Δl. For $\Delta j \geq \Delta l$ the smallest value of L is $\Delta l + 2$, and, in addition, we must have $\Delta l \leq j + j' - 2$. Thus, if $\Delta l = \Delta j = 0$ we have electric quadrupole radiation provided that $j + j' = 2j \geq 2$; that is, $j \neq \frac{1}{2}$. Otherwise only magnetic radiation is possible and dipole radiation will be most important. These selection rules apply to odd mass nuclei. Even mass nuclei are discussed below.

The analysis of the selection rules for magnetic radiation is easily obtained from (6.30a)–(6.30e). The general rules are $\Delta(jj'L)$ and $L + \Delta l$ an odd integer. The triangle condition $\Delta(lL\,l'+1)$ does permit $L = \Delta l - 1$ for $l > l'$, $\Delta l = l - l'$ which implies $l - l' \geq 2$. However, for this value of L, the condition $L \geq \Delta j$ is fulfilled only in case iv, and in this case $B = 0$ for the assumed value of L. Consequently, the minimum value of L is $L_{min} = \Delta l + 1$. For $l' \geq l$ the C-coefficient in (6.30a) requires $L \geq \Delta l + 1$. Hence $L_{min} = \Delta l + 1$ in general. If $j + j' < \Delta l + 1$ no magnetic radiation is possible and pure electric radiation occurs. An example is the $s_{1/2} \leftrightarrow d_{3/2}$ transition. In general, for these "forbidden" magnetic transitions either the initial (or final) state is $s_{1/2}$, and for the final (or initial) state $j = l - \frac{1}{2}$ (or $j' = l' - \frac{1}{2}$) with $L = l - 1$ (or $l' - 1$).

The selection rules imply that the transitions $s_{1/2} \rightarrow s_{1/2}$ and $p_{1/2} \rightarrow p_{1/2}$ involve pure magnetic dipole emission while $s_{1/2} \leftrightarrow p_{1/2}$ involves pure electric dipole radiation. These results are seen to be an immediate consequence of angular momentum and parity conservation. On the other hand the impossibility of such transitions as $s_{1/2} \leftrightarrow d_{3/2}$ with the emission of magnetic dipole radiation is a consequence of the assumptions made concerning the nuclear forces. For instance, such transitions are permitted if the forces contain a term of the spin-orbit coupling type [i.e., a term proportional to $\boldsymbol{\sigma}\cdot\mathbf{L}$; see Jensen and Mayer (52)].[2]

For even mass nuclei with integer j and j' the selection rule embodied in $\Delta(Ljj')$, which is an immediate consequence of the Eckart theorem, together with the parity selection rule, implies pure 2^L pole radiation if either $j = 0$ or $j' = 0$. In such cases $L = \Delta j$ is the only possibility. The radiation is pure electric if the initial and final state parities, π_i and π_f, fulfill $\pi_i \pi_f = (-)^L$ and pure magnetic if $\pi_i \pi_f = (-)^{L+1}$.

When the transition does not correspond to pure multipole emission there will be a mixture of effectively two multipoles which, in some cases, may have comparable intensity. It is of interest to examine the foregoing results from this point of view. For this purpose we need at least an approximate evaluation of the radial integrals $\mathfrak{M}_L$. Estimates of these radial integrals have been given by Moszkowski (53) for several models, and his results show that $\mathfrak{M}_L \sim 0.4$ to 0.5 for all models investigated and is rather insensitive to the value of L. With this fact in mind we may compare (6.30) and (6.22) to obtain a rough estimate of the relative intensity of an ML versus an $E(L+1)$ radiation. This is

$$\frac{I(M, L)}{I(E, L+1)} = \frac{\tau(E, L+1)}{\tau(M, L)} \sim \frac{(2L+3)^2}{(kR)^4}\left(\frac{\hbar k}{M_p c}\right)^2 \tag{6.31}$$

For $R = 1.2 \times 10^{-13} A^{1/3}$ cm and $\hbar\omega$ in Mev, the ratio (6.31) is

$$\frac{I(M, L)}{I(E, L+1)} \sim \left[\frac{25(2L+3)}{(\hbar\omega)_{\text{Mev}} A^{2/3}}\right]^2 \tag{6.31$'$}$$

This is essentially the result obtained by Austern and Sachs (51) from somewhat different considerations. For $\hbar\omega = 100$ kev and $A \sim 30$ the ratio of magnetic dipole to electric quadrupole intensities would thus be estimated as 10^4, and for $L > 1$ the magnetic multipole intensity

[2] The interaction term is then proportional to $\boldsymbol{\sigma}\cdot\mathbf{r} \times \mathbf{A}$. From (6.8) and (3.4) this is seen to be $\boldsymbol{\sigma}\cdot\mathbf{r} \times (\mathbf{r} \times \nabla) Y_L^M$, within a factor which is irrelevant from the point of view of selection rules. From (2.47) and (2.58) it follows that the spin-angular part of the pertinent operator is

$$\boldsymbol{\sigma}\cdot\{\sqrt{L}\, \mathbf{T}_{L,L+1}^M + \sqrt{L+1}\, \mathbf{T}_{L,L-1}^M\}$$

The matrix elements of this operator have been evaluated in j-j coupling by Rose and Osborn (54). For the $s_{1/2} \leftrightarrow d_{3/2}$ transition with the emission of $M1$ radiation the first term makes a non-vanishing contribution. In general this term contributes to $s_{1/2} \leftrightarrow l_{l-1/2}$ with $L = l - 1$, and the second term makes no contribution.

would predominate even more strongly. For 1-Mev radiation from heavy nuclei the ratio (6.31′) is of order 10 for $L = 1$. Inasmuch as the possibility of an overestimation by a factor of this order is possible in the rough evaluation which led to (6.31′) it is not too surprising that the experimental evidence does show that the $M1$ and $E2$ intensities may be comparable in some cases. In this connection it should be emphasized that the measured lifetime τ_T is given by

$$1/\tau_T = (1/\tau)(1 + \alpha)$$

where α is the internal conversion coefficient; see Chapter V. When there is a mixture of two multipoles in the radiation field, ML and $E(L + 1)$ say, the internal conversion coefficient is

$$\alpha = \frac{I(M, L)\,\alpha(M, L) + I(E, L{+}1)\,\alpha(E, L{+}1)}{I(M, L) + I(E, L{+}1)}$$

where the conversion coefficients for the pure multipoles are given by Rose, Goertzel, et al. (51). In practice, the intensity ratio for ML and $E(L + 1)$ radiations is determined by a comparison of the measured α and the calculated conversion coefficients for pure multipoles, or by comparison of observation and theory in the angular correlation of two successively emitted radiations, one of which is the mixed multipole transition; cf. Biedenharn and Rose (53) and sec. 32.

32. ANGULAR DISTRIBUTION OF THE RADIATION

On physical grounds it is obvious that, if no direction in space is preferred, the emitted radiation will be isotropic. However, there are two circumstances of particular interest wherein a preferred direction may exist. The first is the angular correlation process in which the radiation is detected in coincidence with another radiation the propagation vector of which serves to single out the preferred direction. The second case of interest is that in which the emitting nucleus is situated in an electric or magnetic field which provides the unique direction. The magnetic field may be an external one or may be a result of the combined action of an external field which polarizes surrounding electrons, and these, by the hyperfine coupling, polarize the nucleus. In the absence of such fields the nuclear energy levels, of angular momentum j', exhibit a $(2j' + 1)$fold degeneracy corresponding to the isotropy of space. In the presence of the fields these levels are split, and, under the equilibrium Boltzmann distribution, the population $p_{m'}$ of the substates of the initial state, with quantum numbers j', m', will depend on m'. The electric field may be provided by the electric quadrupole interaction in single crystals [Pound (49)] or by the anisotropic hyperfine structure interaction of paramagnetic ions in single crystals [Bleaney (51)]. For these electrostatic interactions the perturbation is unchanged when all spins are reversed in direction and $p_{m'}$ depends only on $|m'|$. The type of orientation in such cases is referred to as an "alignment" in contrast to the magnetic orientation where $p_{m'}$ will, in general, depend on the sign of m' and where one speaks of a "polarization."

In all the cases of orientation referred to there is a natural choice for the direction of the quantization axis, and we take it to be along the preferred direction. We therefore consider the intensity of electromagnetic radiation emitted in a transition from a state $j'm'$ to a state jm, and the projection quantum number of the radiation, which now has an observational significance, is $M = m - m'$. The intensity per unit solid angle will be proportional to

$$\mathcal{I} = \sum_{m'M} p_{m'} |(jm|\mathfrak{H}(\mathbf{A})|jm')|^2 \tag{6.32}$$

where $\mathfrak{H}(\mathbf{A})$ is an operator linear in the vector potential $\mathbf{A}$ of a plane wave. For greater generality we consider that the plane wave is detected by a polarimeter which measures its state of linear polarization. A Compton scatterer interposed between source and detector provides one example of such a detection method. The vector potential is then

$$\mathbf{A} = \frac{1}{\sqrt{2}} \sum_P e^{-iP\phi}\, \mathbf{A}_P = \boldsymbol{\epsilon}\, e^{i\mathbf{k}\cdot\mathbf{r}} \tag{6.33}$$

where $\mathbf{A}_P$ represents a circularly polarized wave, and is given in (6.8). The unit polarization vector is, cf. (6.4),

$$\boldsymbol{\epsilon} = \mathbf{u}_1 \cos\phi + \mathbf{u}_2 \sin\phi$$

and ϕ is the angle between the electric field and $\mathbf{u}_1$. That is, $\mathbf{u}_1$ is the direction defined by the intersection of the plane normal to $\mathbf{k}$ and the plane of $\mathbf{k}$ and the quantization axis. The direction of $\mathbf{u}_1$ along this line is irrelevant for our purpose.

Using (6.8) and the Eckart theorem the matrix element in (6.32) becomes

$$(jm|\mathfrak{H}(\mathbf{A})|j'm') = \frac{\pi}{\sqrt{2}} \sum_{LMP} i^L \sqrt{2L+1}\, e^{-iP\phi}\, D^L_{MP}(\mathbf{k}_1)\, C(j'Lj; m'M)$$
$$\times [(j\|\mathfrak{H}(\mathbf{A}_L(m))\|j') + iP(j\|\mathfrak{H}(\mathbf{A}_L(e)\|j')] \tag{6.34}$$

The square brackets in (6.34) contain the reduced matrix elements.

We consider a specific pair of substates m and m' and, to begin with, pure multipole emission. Then only a single value of L and M are involved in the sum (6.34). In this case

$$\mathcal{I} = \sum_{m'M} p_{m'} \mathcal{I}_{m'M}(\tau) \tag{6.35}$$

where

$$\mathcal{I}_{m'M}(\tau) = \frac{\pi^2}{2} (2L+1)\{C(j'Lj; m'M) \,|\, (j\|\mathfrak{H}(\mathbf{A}_L(\tau))\|j') \,|\}^2 F_L^M(\mathbf{k}_1) \tag{6.35a}$$

with

$$F_L^M(\mathbf{k}_1) = |\sum_P P^\sigma e^{-iP\phi} D_{MP}^L|^2 \tag{6.35b}$$

and $\sigma = 1$ for electric multipoles while $\sigma = 0$ for magnetic multipoles. Of course, $P = \pm 1$ only. The functions F_L^M give the angular dependence of the emitted intensity and are referred to as radiation patterns.

Applying the Clebsch-Gordan series (2.30) the radiation patterns become

$$F_L^M(\mathbf{k}_1) = 2(-)^{M+1} \sum_\nu C(LL\nu; M, -M)\{C(LL\nu; 1, -1)P_\nu(\cos\vartheta) + (-)^\sigma C(LL\nu; 11) \sqrt{\frac{(\nu-2)!}{(\nu+2)!}} \cos 2\phi \, P_\nu^2(\cos\vartheta)\} \tag{6.36}$$

Here ϑ is the angle between $\mathbf{k}_1$ and the quantization axis. In obtaining this result use is made of the following:

$$\sum_P C(LL\nu; P, -P) = [1 + (-)^\nu] \, C(LL\nu; 1, -1)$$

from (2.20b). Hence, in (6.36) the sum index ν takes on only even values. This implies symmetry of the angular distribution with respect to $\vartheta = \pi/2$. Moreover, $\nu \leq 2L$, because of $\Delta(LL\nu)$, and in the second term, which represents the polarization dependent part of the intensity, $\nu \geq 2$. In addition we have used

$$D_{02}^\nu(\mathbf{k}_1) = D_{02}^\nu(\varphi\vartheta 0) = D_{20}^{\nu *}(0, -\vartheta, -\varphi) = D_{-20}^\nu(0, -\vartheta, -\varphi) = \sqrt{\frac{4\pi}{2\nu+1}} Y_\nu^2(\vartheta, 0) = \sqrt{\frac{(\nu-2)!}{(\nu+2)!}} P_\nu^2(\cos\vartheta)$$

by (2.28) and (2.31). Here P_ν^2 is the well-known associated Legendre polynomial: $P_\nu^2 = \sin^2 \vartheta d^2 P_\nu / d(\cos \vartheta)^2$.

From (6.36) it is seen that the shapes of the angular distribution for electric and magnetic multipoles differ only for polarized radiation. For unpolarized radiation the average over ϕ removes the second term and the dependence on the character of the radiation which is represented by the phase factor $(-)^\sigma$. It is to be noted that for pure multipole emission the reduced matrix elements enter only as scale factors and do not affect the shape of the angular distribution. The normalization of the radiation pattern is

$$\int F_L^M(\mathbf{k}_1)\, d\Omega = \frac{8\pi}{2L+1}$$

For emission of mixed multipoles such as ML and $E(L+1)$ two terms of (6.34) are necessary, and we obtain

$$\begin{aligned} \mathcal{I}_{m'M}(e, m) &= \frac{\pi^2}{2}(2L+1)\{C(j'Lj; m'M)\,|\,(j\|\mathfrak{H}(\mathbf{A}_L(m))\|j')\,|\}^2 F_L^M(\mathbf{k}_1, m) \\ &+ \frac{\pi^2}{2}(2L+3)\{C(j'\,L{+}1\,j; m'M)\,|\,(j\|\mathfrak{H}(\mathbf{A}_{L+1}(e))\|j')\,|\}^2 F_{L+1}^M(\mathbf{k}_1, e) \\ &+ \pi^2\sqrt{(2L+1)(2L+3)}\; C(j'Lj; m'M)\; C(j'\,L{+}1\,j; m'M) \\ &\times Re(j\|\mathfrak{H}(\mathbf{A}_L(m))\|j')(j\|\mathfrak{H}(\mathbf{A}_{L+1}(e))\|j')^*\, F_{L,L+1}^M(\mathbf{k}_1) \end{aligned} \tag{6.37}$$

Here $F_L^M(\mathbf{k}_1, m)$ and $F_{L+1}^M(\mathbf{k}_1, e)$ represent the radiation patterns for pure ML and pure $E(L+1)$ radiation respectively; cf. (6.36). The third term represents interference between the two multipoles. In this term "*Re*" indicates real part. The interference radiation pattern is

$$F_{L,L+1}^M(\mathbf{k}_1) = -\sum_{PP'} P'\, e^{i(P'-P)\phi}\, D_{MP}^L\, D_{MP'}^{L+1*}$$

This is again evaluated by using the Clebsch-Gordan series and (2.20*b*). One obtains

$$\begin{aligned} F_{L,L+1}^M(\mathbf{k}_1) &= -2(-)^{M+1}\sum_\nu C(L\,L{+}1\,\nu; M, -M) \\ &\times \Big\{C(L\,L{+}1\,\nu; 1, -1)\,P_\nu(\cos\vartheta) - C(L\,L{+}1\,\nu; 11) \\ &\times \sqrt{\frac{(\nu-2)!}{(\nu+2)!}}\cos 2\phi\, P_\nu^2(\cos\vartheta)\Big\} \end{aligned} \tag{6.38}$$

Again, ν is even and in both terms $2 \leq \nu \leq 2L$. Since the total intensity is obtained by integrating over all directions of $\mathbf{k}_1$, so that only the $\nu = 0$ term contributes, it follows that the interference term does not contribute to the total intensity. In contrast to the case of pure multipoles the shape of the angular distribution depends on ratio of reduced matrix elements for the two multipoles of the mixture.

Specific results for the angular distribution follow when the population function $p_{m'}$ is specified; cf. Steenberg (52). Without entering into these details it is easy to see that only the part of $p_{m'}$ even in m' is relevant. Thus, the intensity in a given direction will be proportional to

$$\mathcal{S} = \sum_{m'M} (-)^M p_{m'}\, C(j'Lj; m'M)\, C(j'L'j; m'M)\, C(LL'\nu; M, -M) \quad (6.39)$$

where $L' = L$ for the self-terms and $L' = L + 1$ for the interference term. Since m' and M are summation letters which have limits symmetrical with respect to 0, their signs may be changed. Then, if (2.20*b*) is applied, the signs of m' and M in the C-coefficients are brought back to the form in which they appear in (6.39) and a phase factor

$$(-)^{j'+L-j}(-)^{j'+L'-j}(-)^{L+L'-\nu} = (-)^{\nu} = 1$$

is introduced. Since M is an integer the net result is that $p_{m'}$ is changed to $p_{-m'}$. Hence, $p_{m'}$ in (6.39) may be replaced by $\frac{1}{2}(p_m + p_{-m'})$. Consequently, the alignment technique for which $p_{m'} = p_{-m'}$ constitutes no restriction so far as obtaining anisotropic radiation is concerned. On the other hand, if $j' = \frac{1}{2}$ then $p_{m'} + p_{-m'} = p_{\frac{1}{2}} + p_{-\frac{1}{2}}$ is independent of m'. Consequently, in this case the situation is the same as if the populations of the substates were uniform. For constant $p_{m'}$, as is to be expected, only an isotropic distribution will be obtained. That this result actually does appear may be checked by observing that when $p_{m'}$ = constant the sum in (6.39) may be carried out directly by the technique described in sec. 11. Two Racah recouplings accomplished by means of (2.54) show that for constant $p_{m'}$ the sum $\mathcal{S}$ is proportional to

$$\sum_{M} (-)^M C(L'L'\nu; M, -M) = (-)^{L'} \sqrt{2L' + 1}\, \delta_{\nu 0}$$

by use of

$$C(L'L'0; M, -M) = (-)^{L'-M}/\sqrt{2L' + 1}$$

and the orthogonality rule (2.17). The $\nu = 0$ term in the radiation patterns contains only $P_0 = 1$ and gives isotropy.

The relation between the reduced matrix elements and the total intensity may be seen by integrating over all directions of emission and carrying out the summations over m' and M in (6.35). The total intensity is then proportional to

$$\mathcal{I}_T = \int d\Omega\, \mathcal{I} = 4\pi^3\{|(j\|\mathfrak{H}(\mathbf{A}_L(m))\|j')|^2 \sum_{m'M} p_{m'}\, C^2(j'Lj; m'M) + |(j\|\mathfrak{H}(\mathbf{A}_{L+1}(e))\|j')|^2 \sum_{m'M} p_{m'}\, C^2(j'\, L{+}1\, j; m'M)\}$$

Carrying out the M summation after interchange of j' and j in the C-coefficients, we obtain

$$\sum_{m'M} p_{m'}\, C^2(j'L'j; m'M) = \frac{2j+1}{2j'+1} \sum_{m'} p_{m'}$$

where $L' = L$ or $L + 1$. The latter sum is merely the total population of the initial state which we normalize to $2j' + 1$. Hence,

$$\mathcal{I}_T = 4\pi^3(2j+1)\{|(j\|\mathfrak{H}(\mathbf{A}_L(m))\|j')|^2 + (j\|\mathfrak{H}(\mathbf{A}_{L+1}(e))\|j')|^2\}$$

Thus, the square moduli of the reduced matrix elements are proportional to the respective multipole intensities, and their ratio is precisely the relative intensity of the two multipoles.

APPENDIX A. SIGN CONVENTIONS

In adopting a set of sign conventions for the orbital angular-momentum eigenfunctions Y_L^M, the C-coefficients (sec. 7), and hence the W-coefficients (sec. 11) and the rotation matrices introduced in sec. 8 it is obviously necessary to be consistent. It is also desirable that the adopted conventions agree, so far as possible, with already existing definitions. This desideratum has motivated the choice made throughout this book. To facilitate comparison with other choices the following remarks may be made.

The definition of Y_L^M given in (1.18) differs from that used in Bethe (33) and Rose (37) by a phase factor $(-)^M$ and agrees with the definition of Condon and Shortley (35). The vector addition or C-coefficients are identical with those of the latter reference and hence identical with those used by Racah, (42) and (43). In particular, the choice of phase is in accord with

$$C(j_1j_2\,j_1+j_2;j_1j_2) = 1 \tag{A.1}$$

The rotation matrices $D^j_{m'm}$ are so chosen as to agree with Wigner (31). Note, however, that Wigner used a left-handed coordinate system. The definition given in sec. 8 is equivalent to

$$D^j_{m'm}(\alpha\beta\gamma) = (jm'|\,e^{iJ_z\alpha}\,e^{iJ_y\beta}\,e^{iJ_z\gamma}\,|jm) \tag{A.2}$$

and, in order that the customary commutation rules for the angular-momentum operators be valid, the rotation γ around the z-axis is a counterclockwise rotation as seen from the positive z-axis. That is, a rotation $\gamma = \pi/2$ brings the x-axis into the direction of the positive y-axis. This is the reason for the negative angles $-\beta$, $-\alpha$ in the spherical harmonic addition theorem as it appears in sec. 8. Goertzel (46) uses the definition

$$D^j_{m'm}(\alpha\beta\gamma) = (jm|\,e^{-iJ_z\gamma}\,e^{-iJ_y\beta}\,e^{-iJ_z\alpha}\,|jm') \tag{A.3}$$

In comparing (A.2) with other definitions it is to be noted that the replacement of α, β, γ with $-\gamma$, $-\beta$, $-\alpha$ implies replacing D by the inverse matrix, and this is what must be done when a given rotation of the coordinate axes is replaced by an equivalent rotation of the field. Because the inverse rotation is carried out on the field rather than on the coordinate axes it is not necessary to introduce the J_y and J_z operators in a rotated frame of reference. All the operators in (A.2) refer to the same coordinate system.

APPENDIX B. EXPLICIT *C*- AND *W*-COEFFICIENTS

For purposes of convenience the explicit forms of the vector addition or *C*-coefficients (sec. 7) and Racah or *W*-coefficients (sec. 11) are given here. These are conveniently given in terms of hypergeometric functions. The latter are [1]

$$ {}_pF_q(a_1 \cdots a_p; b_1 \cdots b_q; z) = \sum_{\nu=0}^{\infty} \frac{a_1(\nu)a_2(\nu) \cdots a_p(\nu)}{b_1(\nu)b_2(\nu)b_q(\nu)} \frac{z^\nu}{\nu!} \quad \text{(B.1)} $$

where

$$ a_n(\nu) = \frac{(a_n + \nu - 1)!}{(a_n - 1)!} $$

et simile. The reciprocal of $(-c)!$ where c is a positive integer is equal to zero. If any of the a_n are negative integers then ${}_pF_q$ is a polynomial. Of course, if any b_n is a negative integer there must be a negative integer $a_n \geq b_n$.

In terms of these functions

$$ \begin{aligned} C(j_1j_2j; m_1m_2) &= (-)^{j_2+m_2} \\ &\times \sqrt{\frac{(j+j_1-j_2)!(j_1+j_2-j)!(j-m)!(j_1-m_1)!(2j+1)}{(j-j_1+j_2)!(j_1+j_2+j+1)!(j+m)!(j_1+m_1)!(j_2-m_2)!(j_2+m_2)!}} \\ &\times \frac{(j+j_2+m_1)!}{(j_1-j_2-m)!} {}_3F_2(-j+j_1-j_2, j_1-m_1+1, -j-m; \\ &\qquad j_1-j_2-m+1, -j-j_2-m_1; 1) \end{aligned} \quad \text{(B.2)} $$

If $m_1 = m_2 = 0$ we obtain

$$ C(abc; 00) = (-)^{\frac{1}{2}(a+b-c)} \sqrt{\frac{2c+1}{a+b+c+1}} \times \frac{\tau(a+b+c)}{\tau(a+b-c)\,\tau(a-b+c)\,\tau(-a+b+c)} \quad \text{(B.3)} $$

[1] The properties of the *C*- and *W*-coefficients given in the text may be obtained using the well-known properties of the hypergeometric functions. The properties of the hypergeometric functions are summarized by Bailey (35).

where

$$\tau(x) = \frac{(x/2)!}{\sqrt{x!}}$$

and a, b, and c are integers with an even sum.

For the W-coefficient we obtain

$$W(abcd; ef) = \frac{t(abe)\, t(cde)\, t(acf)\, t(bdf)(a + b + c + d + 1)!}{(e + f - a - d)!(e + f - b - c)!}$$
$$\times\, {}_4F_3(-a - b + e,\ -c - d + e,\ -a - c + f,\ -b - d + f;$$
$$-a - b - c - d - 1,\ e + f - a - d + 1,\ e + f - b - c + 1;\ 1) \tag{B.4}$$

Here

$$t(abe) = \sqrt{\frac{(a - b + e)!(-a + b + e)!}{(a + b - e)!(a + b + e + 1)!}}$$

Both C and W are polynomials for all arguments finite.

Particular results of importance are obtained from these formulas when one of the six parameters is ½ or 1. These results, taken from Biedenharn, Blatt, and Rose (52), are given in Tables BI and BII.

TABLE BI. $W(abcd; \frac{1}{2}f)$

	$a = b + \frac{1}{2}$	$a = b - \frac{1}{2}$
$c = d + \frac{1}{2}$	$(-)^{b+d-f}\sqrt{\dfrac{(b+d+f+2)(b+d-f+1)}{(2b+1)(2b+2)(2d+1)(2d+2)}}$	$(-)^{b+d-f}\sqrt{\dfrac{(f-b+d+1)(f+b-d)}{2b(2b+1)(2d+1)(2d+2)}}$
$c = d - \frac{1}{2}$	$(-)^{b+d-f}\sqrt{\dfrac{(f+b-d+1)(f-b+d)}{(2b+1)(2b+2)2d(2d+1)}}$	$(-)^{b+d-f-1}\sqrt{\dfrac{(b+d+f+1)(b+d-f)}{2b(2b+1)2c(2c+1)}}$

TABLE BII. $W(abcd; 1f)$

	$c = d + 1$
$a = b + 1$	$(-)^{b+d-f}\sqrt{\dfrac{(f+b+d+3)(f+b+d+2)(-f+b+d+2)(-f+b+d+1)}{4(2b+3)(b+1)(2b+1)(2d+3)(d+1)(2d+1)}}$
$a = b$	$(-)^{b+d-f}\sqrt{\dfrac{(f+b+d+2)(-f+b+d+1)(f-b+d+1)(f+b-d)}{4b(2b+1)(b+1)(2d+1)(d+1)(2d+3)}}$
$a = b - 1$	$(-)^{b+d-f}\sqrt{\dfrac{(f+b-d)(f+b-d-1)(f-b+d+2)(f-b+d+1)}{4(2b+1)(2b-1)b(d+1)(2d+1)(2d+3)}}$
	$c = d$
$a = b + 1$	$(-)^{b+d-f}\sqrt{\dfrac{(f+b+d+2)(f+b-d+1)(b+d-f+1)(f-b+d)}{4(2b+1)(b+1)(2b+3)d(d+1)(2d+1)}}$
$a = b$	$(-)^{b+d-f}\dfrac{b(b+1)+d(d+1)-f(f+1)}{\sqrt{4b(b+1)(2b+1)d(d+1)(2d+1)}}$
$a = b - 1$	$(-)^{b+d-f-1}\sqrt{\dfrac{(b+d+f+1)(b+d-f)(f+b-d)(f-b+d+1}{4(2b+1)b(2b-1)d(2d+1)(d+1)}}$
	$c = d - 1$
$a = b + 1$	$(-)^{b+d-f}\sqrt{\dfrac{(f-b+d)(f-b+d-1)(f+b-d+2)(f+b-d+1)}{4(2b+1)(b+1)(2b+3)(2d-1)d(2d+1)}}$
$a = b$	$(-)^{b+d-f-1}\sqrt{\dfrac{(f+b+d+1)(f+b-d+1)(f+d-b)(b+d-f)}{4b(2b+1)(b+1)d(2d+1)(2d-1)}}$
$a = b - 1$	$(-)^{b+d-f}\sqrt{\dfrac{(f+b+d+1)(f+b+d)(-f+b+d)(-f+b+d-1)}{4(2b+1)b(2b-1)(2d+1)d(2d-1)}}$

REFERENCES

References concerned primarily with the general theory of multipole fields are marked with an asterisk.

Abraham, M., (14), *Physik. Z.*, *15*, 914 (1914).

Alder, K., and A. Winther, (53), *Phys. Rev.*, *91*, 1578 (1953).

Austern, N., and R. G. Sachs, (51), *Phys. Rev.*, *81*, 710 (1951).

Bailey, W. N., (35), *Generalized Hypergeometric Series*, Cambridge University Press, 1935.

Bethe, H. A., (33), *Handbuch der Physik*, Vol. 24/1, Springer, Berlin, 1933.

*Berestetski, V. B., (47), *J. Phys. U.S.S.R.*, *11*, 85 (1947).

Berestetski, V. B., (48), *J. Exptl. Theoret. Phys. U.S.S.R.*, *18*, 1057 (1948). (In Russian.)

Biedenharn, L. C., (51), Oak Ridge National Laboratory Report 1098.

Biedenharn, L. C., J. M. Blatt, and M. E. Rose, (52), *Revs. Modern Phys.*, *24*, 249 (1952).

Biedenharn, L. C., and M. E. Rose, (53), *Revs. Modern Phys.*, *25*, 729 (1953).

*Blaton, J., (37), *Acta Phys. Polon.*, *6*, 256 (1937).

*Blatt, J. M., and V. F. Weisskopf, (52), *Theoretical Nuclear Physics*, Appendix B, John Wiley & Sons, New York, 1952.

Bleaney, B., (51), *Proc. Phys. Soc. (London)*, *A64*, 315 (1951).

Brennan, J. G., and R. G. Sachs, (52), *Phys. Rev.*, *88*, 824 (1952).

*Brinkmann, H., (32), *Zur Quantenmechanik der Multipolstrahlung*, Proefschrift, Utrecht, 1932.

Casimir, H. B. G., (36), *Archives der Musée Teyler*, Series III, VIII.

Coish, H. R., (51), Ph.D. dissertation, University of Manitoba.

Condon, E. U., and G. H. Shortley, (35), *Theory of Atomic Spectra*, Cambridge University Press, London, 1935.

Corben, H. C., and J. S. Schwinger, (40), *Phys. Rev.*, *58*, 953 (1940).

Dancoff, S. M., and P. Morrison, (39), *Phys. Rev.*, *55*, 122 (1939).

*DeWitt, C. M., and J. H. D. Jensen, (53), *Z. Naturforsch.*, *8a*, 267 (1953).

Eckart, C., (30), *Revs. Modern Phys.*, *2*, 305 (1930).

Falkoff, D. L., and G. E. Uhlenbeck, (50), *Phys. Rev.*, *79*, 323 (1950).

Fierz, M., (49), *Helv. Phys. Acta*, *22*, 489 (1949).

*Franz, W., (50), *Z. Physik*, *127*, 363 (1950).

*French, J. B., and Y. Shimamoto, (53), *Phys. Rev.*, *91*, 898 (1953).

Goertzel, G., (46), *Phys. Rev.*, *70*, 897 (1946).

*Hansen, W. W., (35), *Phys. Rev.*, *47*, 139 (1935).

*Heitler, W., (36), *Proc. Cambridge Phil. Soc.*, *32*, 112 (1936).

Hulme, H. R., (36), *Proc. Roy. Soc. (London)*, *A154*, 487 (1936).

*Humblet, J., (44), *Physica*, *11*, 91, 100 (1944).

Jensen, J. H. D., and M. G. Mayer, (52), *Phys. Rev.*, *85*, 1040 (1952).

*Kramers, H. A., (43), *Physica*, *10*, 261 (1943).

Massey, H. M. S., and E. H. S. Burhop, (36), *Proc. Roy. Soc. (London)*, *A148*, 272 (1936).

Mayer, M. G., (50), *Phys. Rev.*, *78*, 16, 22 (1950).

*Mie, G., (08), *Ann. Physik*, *25*, 377 (1908).
Morse, P. M., and H. Feshbach, (53), *Methods of Theoretical Physics*, Part II, §13.3, McGraw-Hill, New York, 1953.
Moszkowski, S., (53), *Phys. Rev.*, *89*, 474 (1953).
Pound, R. V., (49), *Phys. Rev.*, *76*, 140 (1949).
Pound, R. V., (50), *Phys. Rev.*, *79*, 685 (1950).
Racah, G., (42), *Phys. Rev.*, *62*, 438 (1942).
Racah, G., (43), *Phys. Rev.*, *63*, 367 (1943).
Rose, M. E., (37), *Phys. Rev.*, *51*, 484 (1937).
Rose, M. E., (49), *Phys. Rev.*, *76*, 678 (1949); *78*, 184 (1950).
Rose, M. E., (51), *Phys. Rev.*, *82*, 389 (1951).
Rose, M. E., G. Goertzel, B. Spinrad, J. Harr, and P. Strong, (51), *Phys. Rev.*, *83*, 79 (1951).
Rose, M. E., (54), *Proc. Phys. Soc.*, *A67*, 239 (1954).
Rose, M. E., and R. K. Osborn, (54), *Phys. Rev.*, *93*, 1315 (1954).
Sachs, R. G., and N. Austern, (51), *Phys. Rev.*, *81*, 705 (1951).
Schiff, L., (49), *Quantum Mechanics*, McGraw-Hill, New York, 1949.
Sharp, W. T., J. M. Kennedy, B. J. Sears, and M. G. Hoyle, (53), Report CRT-556 (Chalk River).
Siegert, A. J. F., (37), *Phys. Rev.*, *52*, 787 (1937).
Stech, B., (52), *Z. Naturforsch.*, *7a*, 401 (1952).
Steenberg, N. R., (52), *Proc. Phys. Soc. (London)*, *A65*, 791 (1952).
*Stratton, J. A., (41), *Electromagnetic Theory*, Chapter VIII, McGraw-Hill, New York, 1941.
Tralli, N., and G. Goertzel, (51), *Phys. Rev.*, *83*, 399 (1951).
*Wallace, P. R., (51), *Can. J. Phys.*, *29*, 393 (1951).
Wentzel, G., (46), *Quantentheorie der Wellenfelder*, J. W. Edwards, Ann Arbor, 1946.
Weyl, H., (39), *The Classical Groups*, Princeton University Press, 1939.
Wigner, E. P., (31), *Gruppentheorie*, Friedrich Vieweg und Sohn, Braunschweig, 1931.

INDEX

5/6

7 DAY USE
RET… …DESK FROM WH…

…URN TO …
PHYSICS LIBRA…
This publication is due on the L…
and HOUR stamped below.

FEB 20 1970
MAR 13 1970
AUG 17'70
OCT 28 1971
… 1973
DEC 15 1975
Due end of current quarter
Subject to recall after —
DEC …